ANIMAL ECOLOGY IN TROPICAL AFRICA

PLATE I. A path through the Mabira Forest, Uganda. Many of the trees are over one hundred feet high, and are covered with lianes and epiphytes. This forest is largely evergreen, but some trees are deciduous, losing their leaves in dry weather. Many trees have conspicuous buttresses. The Mabira Forest and other similar forests are rich in mahogany and other economically important timbers; many forests have been cleared of useful trees at least once and then have been allowed to regenerate. Except along paths made by man, grass is absent. Forests like this teem with insects and birds, and monkeys of several species are common; other large mammals are rare or absent. (Photograph by C. H. F. Rowell.)

Animal Ecology in Tropical Africa

D. F. OWEN
Department of Zoology
Makerere University College
Kampala, Uganda, East Africa

W. H. FREEMAN AND COMPANY
SAN FRANCISCO

Published in Great Britain by
Oliver & Boyd Ltd., Edinburgh and London

First published 1966

Printed in Great Britain by
ROBERT CUNNINGHAM AND SONS LTD., Alva

Preface

My aim in this book is to provide an account of some of the ecological problems in tropical Africa. This is not a textbook, but rather an essay around a large and complex subject. As an essay I hope it will be useful to university students in tropical Africa and to more advanced students in schools. Visitors to Africa and some research organisations may also find something of value. I have not written extensively about 'big game', but rather have tried to select examples from the animal kingdom as a whole. Particular emphasis is placed upon peculiarly tropical problems, or on problems that can be best studied in the tropics.

Most of the book is about the work of others, but I have used my own work, chiefly in Uganda, where this seemed appropriate. The reader may find that birds, butterflies, and snails receive disproportionate attention. I make no excuse for this; these are the groups of animals that I happen to know best. The book was written at Makerere University College, Uganda, and I had available only those books, papers, and journals in the libraries of the College. As a result some older works were unavailable, as were most publications in languages other than English.

Some important aspects of ecology are hardly mentioned. The flow of energy between communities is receiving a great deal of attention from ecologists working in the temperate regions, but has not been investigated in tropical Africa. I have not stressed agricultural or medical problems, partly because these have already been or are being treated by others, but I have included a chapter on man. I have excluded mathematical treatment because this has repeatedly appeared in books concerned with general ecology, and as far as I know there are no major mathematical formulations that are peculiar to tropical Africa.

Where possible complex technical terms are avoided. A few are unavoidable and they are defined in the Glossary at the end of the book. Units of measurement are as given in the original work.

v

The text figures were drawn by Jennifer Owen. I am grateful to C. H. F. Rowell and Jennifer Owen for many valuable comments, and to June P. Thurston and L. C. Beadle for some useful suggestions. A grant from the University of East Africa covered the cost of preparing text figures and typing the text.

I am grateful to the following for permission to reproduce published text figures: the Editor of the *Journal of Ecology* (Fig. 3); the Editor, *Revue de Zoologie et de Botanique Africaines* (Fig. 6); the University of Chicago Press (Fig. 8); the Director of the National Museum, Nairobi (Fig. 9); the Editor of *Ibis* and Dr J. Green (Fig. 12); Uganda Shell Limited (Fig. 15); the Permanent Secretary of the Royal Swedish Academy of Science (Fig. 16); the Editor of *Nature* and Dr R. Hartland-Rowe (Fig. 17); Penguin Books Limited (Fig. 19); the Zoological Society of London and Dr G. Fryer (Fig. 23).

D. F. OWEN
Kampala, 1965

Contents

CHAPTER 1

The Biological Scene
Now and in the Past

This book is about Africa between fifteen degrees north and fifteen degrees south of the Equator, a region of great equatorial forests and wide savanna. The area includes some of the largest and deepest lakes in the world and mountains rising to nearly twenty thousand feet. There are great rivers and extensive permanent swamps. Land over six thousand feet, rivers, and lakes of tropical Africa are shown in Fig. 1. Elsewhere in Africa there are vast deserts, some of which just enter the area covered by this book, but these are excluded from discussion, as are the coastal and marine environments, since they present special problems that are not associated with tropical ecology in the strict sense. Madagascar is excluded; most of it is outside the area, and its fauna differs markedly from that of the mainland of Africa.

The northern limit of tropical Africa is the dry and barren Sahara Desert. The desert acts as a barrier between the fauna of tropical Africa and the essentially European fauna of North Africa. The southerly boundary is less well defined, as elements of the tropical African fauna extend south to the Cape. The east and west are bounded by the ocean.

Present Climate and Vegetation

The most important climatic difference between the tropics and the temperate regions is caused by the greater altitude of the sun at midday. On the Equator at midday the sun is never more than $23\frac{1}{2}$ degrees from the vertical. It reaches this low angle at the solstices in December and June, and is directly overhead at the equinoxes in September and March. This means that in those parts of tropical Africa where there are seasonal changes, events are usually repeated twice a year. Seasonal changes in mean daily temperature are small, often no more than a few degrees at the Equator, and are far smaller than the fluctuation experienced during any one day. The most important single climatic factor in the tropics is the amount and regularity of rainfall. In general,

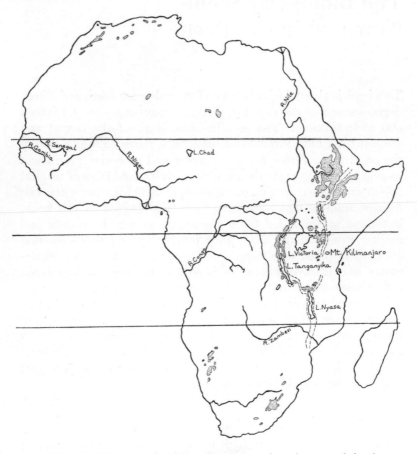

FIG. 1. A map of Africa showing major rivers and land more than 6000 feet above sea level. The Equator and 15° latitude lines are shown. Tropical Africa is here considered to be the geographical area lying between approximately 15° north and 15° south of the Equator. The Rift Valley system is shown by a broken line.

rainfall is of greater ecological importance than temperature in a tropical environment. Much of tropical Africa has a heavy annual rainfall, often exceeding fifty inches, and in areas where the rain is evenly distributed throughout the year there are biological environments, such as evergreen forest, which show little seasonal change. The generally drier savanna country experiences heavy seasonal rain, and in even drier semi-desert or desert country rainfall may be irregular and scarce. Generally speaking, the closer to the Equator, the more even is the distribution of rainfall throughout the year. Large lakes and mountains have a considerable influence on the rainfall pattern in the surrounding areas. And, of course, elevation above sea level has a profound effect on the climate and on the flora and fauna. The climate, vegetation, and animal life on high mountains in some ways parallel those of high latitude regions, but there is a major difference: at high latitudes the major climatic fluctuations are seasonal, whereas high on tropical mountains the major fluctuations, at least in temperature, are diurnal.

Fig. 2 is a vegetation map of tropical Africa; no account is taken of cultivation and destruction of the original vegetation by man. The forested areas include many different types of forest, such as deciduous, semi-deciduous, and evergreen. The humid, mostly evergreen, equatorial forest of west and central Africa reaches its eastern limit (apart from isolated patches) at the western section of the Rift Valley. Most of the forests in the east are high on mountains or around permanent water. The swamp areas are permanent and are often associated with shallow freshwater lakes. Smaller swamps, many of them seasonal, occur throughout the wooded savanna.

The wooded savanna ranges from humid to arid, and there is considerable variation in the vegetation as a result of these climatic differences. Grassy, treeless plains occur within the savanna, and where it merges with the forest it gradually loses its identity. Many of the clumps of trees and shrubs that are so characteristic of the wooded savanna surround an old termite mound. All stages in the colonisation of termite mounds by plants can be found, from a sparse covering of grasses and herbs to a dense tangle of woody shrubs and trees. It is evident that termites are extremely important in determining the distribution of woody vegetation in the savanna. Since termites carry vast quantities of dead vegetation into the underground galleries of their mounds, they may create a small island of rich soil in the otherwise relatively barren savanna. As long as the termite mound is active, damp soil is continually brought to the surface for the construction of new galleries, thus providing a favourable site for the germination of seeds, many of which may have been brought by the termites

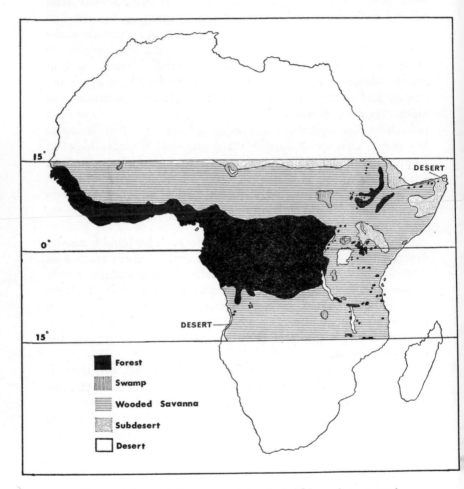

FIG. 2. A vegetation map of tropical Africa. A map such as this is necessarily a generalisation, and the boundaries between vegetational types are in most cases not as sharp as the map would suggest.

themselves or by birds and monkeys that like to sit on the tops of the mounds.

In tropical Africa there are only small areas of desert and sub-desert, and these merge with the wooded savanna.

For more detailed vegetation maps than the one shown in Fig. 2, see Phillips (1959) and Keay (1959). Plate I shows a general view of a path inside mixed semi-deciduous and moist evergreen forest, while Plate II is a general view of the savanna.

Throughout most of tropical Africa the influence of man on the vegetation can be readily seen. Forests are being felled, and cash crops such as coffee and sugar and staple crops such as bananas are replacing the original trees. Tropical forest can regenerate rapidly, but once a forest has been felled there is a tendency for continued exploitation. The savanna is burnt over frequently in the dry season, and in many areas is heavily grazed by domestic animals. Cultivation extends well up the sides of tropical moun-tains, and soil erosion is of widespread occurrence in all these environments.

Past Changes

During the past sixty million years tropical Africa has probably enjoyed greater stability of climate and geology than most other large areas of the world. The glaciations that occurred in the northern regions in the past million years undoubtedly had their effect on the fauna and flora of tropical Africa, but the effect was probably less marked than elsewhere. The few degrees drop in temperature in tropical Africa that must have occurred during the northern glaciations would reduce evaporation and increase the biological effectiveness of the rainfall. As a result, the area of tropical forest would have increased considerably. Many areas of isolated mountain forest in East Africa may have been joined to-gether and also joined to the main west and central equatorial forest at various times during the past million years. Such re-peated joining and fragmentation of the forest must have had im-portant evolutionary and ecological consequences as populations were continually split and joined together again. Lake Chad may within the past ten thousand years have been four times the size of present-day Lake Victoria (Moreau, 1952). There is no doubt from the fossil record that the area at present occupied by the

Sahara Desert had a rich fauna, probably like that of the present East Africa savanna.

Some species of animals now confined to the tropics once occurrred in what are now cold temperate regions: there have in the past been fruit bats, hyaenas, cheetahs, rhinoceroses, crocodiles and ostriches in Europe. The area now occupied by London was once sub-tropical forest. It appears that tropical Africa did not experience the marked fluctuations that have occurred in the composition of the fauna and flora of the temperate regions during the past fifty million years. There has, then, been an enormous amount of time to build up stable and complex biological communities; this long-term stability has undoubtedly had its effect on the composition of the present fauna and flora.

The Present Fauna of Tropical Africa

Any attempt to characterise the fauna of a large area necessarily depends upon the work of competent taxonomists and collectors. The terrestrial vertebrates are better known than most other groups of animals, and for this reason the present fauna of tropical Africa can best be discussed by reference to these animals.

Tropical Africa has a greater array of mammals than any other area of the world. It is particularly rich in large ungulates, primates, and carnivores. The mammals of tropical Africa have closer affinities with those of tropical Asia than with those of any other part of the world. Old world monkeys, apes, pangolins, bamboo rats (Rhizomyidae), elephants, and rhinoceroses are at present found in Africa and Asia and nowhere else in the world. Endemic African mammals include the giraffe, hippopotamus, and aardvark families, three families of insectivores, and six families of rodents. The African savanna is dominated by large numbers of antelopes of many species, and with them are large carnivores, including the big cats and scavengers like hyaenas. The lowland forests contain many monkeys and the chimpanzee; the gorilla is common in places in the highland and lowland forest of west and central Africa. Both fruit-eating and insectivorous bats are abundant. There are no marsupials, and in this respect Africa differs from South America and Australia. There are no true moles, beavers, or bears, all of which occur in the north temperate region. In South America there are groups of mammals that ecologically

PLATE II. Savanna in western Uganda. The scattered clumps of trees and bushes mostly originate from termite mounds, which provide good conditions for seed germination and survival. A euphorbia tree is shown on the right; these and acacias are the most common trees in the savanna. The bushes are thorny and beneath them there is often a dense growth of *Commelira*, a plant that elephants like to eat. Savanna such as this can support large populations of ungulates and their predators. (Photograph by Ministry of Information, Uganda.)

replace certain tropical African groups; these include mammals especially adapted for eating termites yet unrelated to the African pangolins and aardvark, and monkeys of two families not represented in Africa.

The breeding birds of Africa are again more similar to those of tropical Asia than to those of any other part of the world. Thirty per cent of the genera in Africa south of the Sahara are also found in the Asian tropics, but only two per cent of the species are common to both areas (Moreau, 1952). Several families of birds are confined to Africa, including the guinea fowls (seven species), mousebirds (six species), turacos (eighteen species), and woodhoopoes (six species). Four other families of birds, each with a single species, are confined to Africa. Compared with other tropical regions of the world, Africa is rich in bee-eaters, barbets, honeyguides, rollers, weavers, starlings, shrikes, larks, and sunbirds. It has nearly as many hornbills, broadbills, and babblers as tropical Asia, but is relatively poor in fruit pigeons, parrots, kingfishers, trogons, and woodpeckers.

Some tropical African species are replaced by ecologically equivalent but taxonomically unrelated species in other areas of the world. Sunbirds are small, brightly coloured passerine birds with long down-curved bills. They feed on the nectar of flowers and insects associated with nectar. In the American tropics the nectar-feeders are the hummingbirds, which are related to swifts but in colour, superficial structure, behaviour, and ecology closely resemble the sunbirds.

The yellow-throated longclaw, *Macronyx croceus*, is a common bird in the savanna of tropical Africa. It is a ground-nesting species and has an unmistakable voice and flight. It is bright yellow on the underparts with a black band across the upper breast. In the prairies of North America meadowlarks, *Sturnella* spp., occupy the same kind of habitat as the longclaw. They are closely similar to the longclaw in colour and pattern as well as in behaviour, and without doubt fill the niche occupied by the longclaw in Africa.

The vultures of the New World and the vultures of the Old World (including Africa) are closely similar ecologically and in superficial structure. But the two groups differ in important anatomical details and are placed by taxonomists in different suborders. The orioles and flycatchers are also remarkably similar in

Africa and the New World but are placed in different families because of fundamental anatomical differences.

In summary, the birds and mammals of Africa have greatest affinities with those of tropical Asia. African species are frequently replaced by ecologically similar but unrelated species in other parts of the world, especially in North and South America.

Reptiles are essentially tropical animals. Most of the species that occur in temperate regions are closely related to tropical species. Turtles, land tortoises, chameleons and other lizards, snakes, and crocodiles occur in tropical Africa. There are relatively few agamid lizards (although the rainbow lizard, *Agama agama*, is widespread and abundant), but there are many more species of chameleons than anywhere else in the world.

There are many frogs and toads, but no newts and no salamanders, in tropical Africa. The tree frogs of Africa belong to a different family from those of tropical America. The clawed toads, *Xenopus*, are confined to Africa.

The freshwater fish of Africa are extremely varied, and include an endemic family, the Mormyridae, one of the two families of fish that have electric organs used in spatial orientation, and an endemic order, the Polypterini. Lung-fish occur in the swamps and rivers of Africa and are represented by related genera in South America and Australia.

The Past Fauna

Fossils are rare or absent in the humid equatorial regions of the world, simply because conditions are unsuitable for fossilisation. As a result little is known of the past history and distribution of animals in the forests of Africa. Fossils have been found in the drier savanna, particularly in East Africa, and especially in association with freshwater lakes and the dry beds of old lakes. These include land and freshwater molluscs, insects, fish, reptiles, birds, and mammals. There is fossil evidence of many apes in the savanna of East Africa, and it is possible that man had his origins in this region. Many fossil mammals were considerably larger than comparable modern species, but the reasons for this are not known. The distribution of many species has changed in the past million years: several species of aquatic molluscs, fish, and crocodiles once occurred in parts of East Africa where today they are absent.

Thus, in the Kazinga Channel of Western Uganda there can be found great numbers of fossil crocodile teeth, but there are no living crocodiles in the area even though the habitat would appear suitable for them.

As already mentioned, the climate of the Sahara has in the past been much moister than at present. Throughout the Sahara there are traces of human habitation (rock engravings and fossils of domestic animals), fossil elephants, rhinoceroses, hippopotamuses, and giraffes, indicating that within the past ten thousand years the area was much more suitable for animal life than at present.

It must be stressed, however, that the distribution of fossils reflects primarily the distribution of conditions that were suitable for fossilisation. Thus, although many fossil ape-men (or man-apes) have been found in parts of East Africa, it cannot be stated with certainty that the major trends of evolution from ape to man were occurring only in East Africa. The equatorial forests, which have been stable biotic environments for so long, have left no record of the evolutionary changes that must have occurred within them.

Attempts have been made to relate the present distribution of animals in tropical Africa to past climatic changes. The birds of tropical Africa are perhaps better known than any other major group of animals. On the whole the forest birds seem associated with particular vegetation types, and in some cases it is felt that this association can only be explained in terms of past events, in particular of past climatic changes (Moreau, 1963). The difficulty with this approach, which depends upon the existence of geographical variation at the subspecies and species level, is that virtually nothing is known about the rates of speciation and subspeciation in birds. It has been suggested that five thousand years is the time taken for the evolution of a subspecies, but it is possible that this is ten times too long, and in any case no one can agree exactly what constitutes a subspecies.

The Effect of Isolation on the Composition of the Fauna

One important effect of the arrangement of rivers, mountains, and lakes (Fig. 1) and the pattern of the vegetation (Fig. 2) is that tropical Africa is split up into more or less isolated pieces. The fauna of the forest and the savanna have little in common, and there is in many groups of animals, especially invertebrates, little interchange between these two major kinds of habitat. The effects of isolation on the composition of the fauna are best seen by consideration of two areas: high mountains and deep lakes, in which the discontinuity with surrounding environments is marked.

The several isolated mountain masses in tropical Africa (Fig. 1), especially those in East Africa, present biological problems similar to those encountered on oceanic islands. The mountains are islands isolated from each other by hot savanna or humid forest, and in most groups of animals there can be little interchange between adjacent mountains. Species of passerine birds such as white-eyes, *Zosterops*, and thrushes, *Turdus*, are represented by distinct subspecies on adjacent mountains in East Africa (Moreau, 1954), yet in some cases the distance between the mountains is no more than twenty miles. Subspeciation would not be possible unless there was complete or almost complete isolation between these populations.

Mount Kilimanjaro is the highest mountain in Africa. It rises to nearly twenty thousand feet and lies three degrees south of the Equator in East Africa. The mountain is of volcanic origin, and at its base is fifty-two miles from east to west and thirty-six miles from north to south. The hot thorn-bush savanna at its base is at an elevation of four thousand feet; then, proceeding upwards, there is a zone cultivated with coffee and bananas extending to about six thousand feet, followed by a zone of cloud forest to about nine thousand feet. Above the forest there is moorland to about fourteen thousand feet, followed by alpine desert with little vegetation; finally, above sixteen thousand feet, there is little or no life and the summit is under permanent ice. The moorland is occupied by giant species of heaths, groundsels, and related plants that are characteristic of the high mountains of East Africa.

The invertebrate fauna of upper Kilimanjaro has been described by Salt (1954). Some of the species found at high elevation are included in the temperate fauna of Europe and North America, including three species of Collembola, three species of mites, and a fly. A few Kilimanjaro invertebrates are widespread in the lowlands of tropical Africa, and a much greater number are found high on the mountains elsewhere in East Africa, particularly on Ruwenzori, Elgon, and Kenya. Then there are species that are peculiar to Kilimanjaro; all but two of the fifty-four species col-

lected by Salt (1954) and described as new to science have not yet
been found elsewhere. In some cases this may be due to lack of
collecting, but the more conspicuous species, especially the cara-
bid beetles, appear to be endemic. It is possible that the proportion
of endemic species increases with altitude; of the thirty-four species

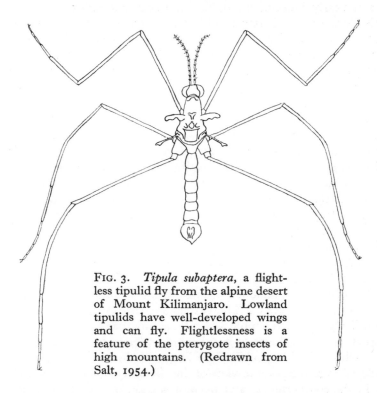

FIG. 3. *Tipula subaptera*, a flightless tipulid fly from the alpine desert
of Mount Kilimanjaro. Lowland
tipulids have well-developed wings
and can fly. Flightlessness is a
feature of the pterygote insects of
high mountains. (Redrawn from
Salt, 1954.)

from the alpine desert zone, nearly two-thirds appear to be endemic.

A great many of the pterygote insects of upper Kilimanjaro
have lost the ability to fly. Loss or reduction of wings is a feature
of the insects of high mountains and oceanic islands; supposedly
the increased windiness results in selection for wing reduction,
but the problem has not been properly studied. On Kilimanjaro
there are flightless moths, beetles, earwigs, tipulid flies, and grasshoppers. A flightless tipulid, *Tipula subaptera*, is shown in Fig. 3.
It is a remarkable insect, quite unlike a lowland 'daddy long legs'.

One evolutionary and ecological effect of flightlessness among high altitude insects is an increase in endemicity, as dispersal to adjacent mountains is prevented.

In the alpine desert zone of Kilimanjaro the temperature falls below freezing on every night of the year. The length of day remains nearly constant throughout the year, and animals living at this elevation are therefore subject to a remarkable and constant climate, unparalleled in the temperate regions or even in the lowland tropics. No invertebrate could be nocturnal because it is always too cold at night. During the day the surface temperature is high and activity of invertebrates tends to be restricted to a few hours in the morning and in the evening. Hibernation and diapause are impossible, as all stages of the life cycle are exposed to the complete range of climate every twenty-four hours. Hence any invertebrate living at this elevation must be adapted in physiology and in behaviour to this remarkable climate. Most species hide under stones during the extremes of cold and heat. The fact that the invertebrate fauna is relatively poor in species on high tropical mountains is perhaps explained by the peculiar climate of these regions; a scarcity in plants available for food may also contribute.

The fauna of the Rift Valley lakes is better known than the fauna of the high mountains. This is partly because the lakes are potentially of economic importance, while the mountains are not, at least not biologically. The two major African Rift lakes, Nyasa and Tanganyika, resemble Lake Baikal in Asia in their physical structure and in the great numbers of endemic species of animals in each. Lake Tanganyika, the larger of the two, may be considered from the point of view of the effect of isolation. The Lake is in the southernmost and deepest section of the Western Rift (Fig. 1), and lies at an elevation of 2,500 feet. It is fourteen thousand square miles in area and 4,600 feet deep at its deepest known point. In many places steep cliffs plunge directly into the Lake. The Lake had its origins about ten million years ago, and, as far as the fauna is concerned, has been isolated for one to six million years, depending on the kinds of evidence used in making a judgement of this kind. Of a total of about one hundred and sixty species, one hundred and thirty-six endemic species of fish have been described from Lake Tanganyika, forty-two of the genera being endemic. About one hundred and fifty species of aquatic mollusc and twenty species of Crustacea are endemic. Endemic oligochaetes, flatworms, sponges, and Protozoa have also been described, but no estimate of the number of endemic species can at present be made because these groups have not yet been studied in detail. Many of the gastropod molluscs have thick ornamented shells reminiscent of marine species, and many of the fish look superficially like the species one might expect on a rocky sea-coast. But the fauna is not of marine origin, and the similarities are the result of convergent evolution. Tanganyika is a large enough expanse of water for the wind to whip up high waves; where these break on the shore, which in places is very rocky with precipitous cliffs, there is considerable resemblance to the sea. A more detailed account of the peculiar fauna of Lake Tanganyika is given in Brooks (1950).

Mount Kilimanjaro and Lake Tanganyika are examples within tropical Africa of areas with striking physical, climatic, and biological features that have resulted in their characteristic fauna. The number of endemic species, especially in the Lake, is high, and provides exceptional opportunities for ecologists who want to investigate species-composition and the effects of isolation.

Evolutionary Considerations

Taking terrestrial and freshwater animals as a whole, most of the species that occur in tropical Africa occur nowhere else in the world. It therefore seems likely that many of these species evolved in tropical Africa. The evolution of species is possible if populations become split and isolated from one another, and if there is adaptation to local environments through natural selection. Tropical Africa has undoubtedly provided many opportunities for speciation through isolation; the enormous numbers of endemic species in the East African lakes testify to this. Another factor that may favour speciation is the number of breeding generations possible in a given period of time. As an example, most European butterflies have one, two, sometimes three generations in a year, whereas tropical African species may have twice as many; in Uganda *Danaus chrysippus* may have as many as twelve generations in a year. Little is known of evolutionary rates in the tropics. In the temperate regions it is known that one allele can be replaced by another through natural selection in fifty to a hundred generations, which may mean fifty to a hundred years in an insect. Because of the increased number of generations it would seem that evolution could potentially be more rapid in the tropics than in the temperate regions. But evolution depends upon environmental changes as well as genetic potentialities; environmental changes may on the whole be slower in the tropics than in the temperate regions. Evidently speciation could occur more rapidly in the tropics, but whether it does is a matter for speculation.

The Biological Scene

What, then, does the animal ecologist find in tropical Africa? He sees vast forests full of animals, some brightly coloured, some cryptic. He sees the savanna, at times very dry and unpleasant for man and at other times extremely wet. He is impressed by the importance of rain in the lives of most animals, and by diurnal changes in temperature that are greater than seasonal changes. Lastly, in almost all areas, he is overwhelmed by the numbers of different species of animals, the subject of the next chapter.

CHAPTER 2

The Number, Abundance, and Diversity of Species

A conspicuous feature of the tropical regions of the world is the large number of species of animals and plants. Many fewer species occur in the temperate regions. Humid tropical lowland forest is by far the richest habitat in the world as regards number of species of animals and plants. Even a casual observer would note that a tropical forest contains far more species than a northern oak or spruce forest.

In 1878 A. R. Wallace, who had vast experience in the tropical regions of the world, wrote: 'Animal life is, on the whole, far more abundant and varied within the tropics than in any other part of the globe, and a great number of peculiar forms are found there which never extend into the temperate regions. Endless eccentricities of form and extreme richness of colour are its most prominent features, and these are manifested in the highest degree in those equatorial lands where the vegetation acquires its greatest beauty and fullest development.'

In this paragraph Wallace appreciates two important features of animal life in the tropics: the great number of species, and the presence of unusual species not found in other parts of the world. Some more recent writers have claimed that each tropical species is rare relative to temperate species, but this claim is in general untrue, for although many tropical species are indeed rare, some others are as abundant as species in temperate regions.

In an English woodland there may be twenty species of tree and woody shrub to the acre, and in eastern North America there are two or three times this number. But in an acre of lowland evergreen forest in tropical Africa there may be as many as three hundred species, and in the forests of South America and tropical

Asia even more. Not only are there more species of trees in tropical forests but also there is a much wider range in the kinds of species; that is to say, there is increased species diversity. It is worthwhile at this point to clarify what is meant by the word 'diversity' in this context. Several recent authors writing of tropical species diversity have discussed only the numbers of species. Diversity means to stand apart in quality, and does not refer to greater numbers of kinds. Diverse species are those that differ in fundamental attributes from other species. There may be in an area a great number of similar species, but this does not represent a great diversity of species. There are in Africa many species of weaver birds, but they are all very similar, and hence there is not much species diversity. On the other hand many of the African birds of prey are very different in form and structure, and hence in this group there is much species diversity.

The vegetation of an area has a profound effect on the number and abundance of animal species. In areas where there are many species of plants and trees there are usually many species of animals, and where there are few plants and trees there are generally fewer species of animals. In general this is because each species of animal is dependent, directly or indirectly, upon relatively few species of plants. Many insects feed on only one species of plant and many predators are restricted to one or a few prey species.

It has been suggested that tropical animal species are better able to tolerate overlapping ecological requirements (Klopfer and MacArthur, 1961); by this hypothesis it is not just the complexity of the habitat that allows the presence of more species in an area; there is in addition an increase in niche-overlap with less exclusive requirements on the part of similar species. There is, however, only slender evidence to support this.

It is useful at this point to compare the number of species in a few selected groups of animals in tropical Africa with comparable groups in temperate regions. It may then be possible to account for the greater number of tropical species in terms of availability of important resources, particularly food. Three groups, mammals, birds, and lycaenid butterflies, will be discussed in this way.

1. *The Mammals of Tanganyika and Britain*

There is a reasonably complete check-list of the land mammals of Tanganyika, including the islands of Zanzibar* (Swynnerton and Hayman, 1950-51). With about two hundred and eighty-nine species of land mammals this area possibly has more than any area of comparable size in the world, and undoubtedly there are many smaller species, particularly bats and rodents, awaiting discovery. By comparison there are about forty-seven species of living native land mammals in Britain, including man, although several other species have been exterminated by man in the last few hundred years.

There are eighty-nine described species of small herbivores in Tanganyika that feed chiefly on leaves, stems, and seeds (especially grass seeds). These include fifty-seven species of rats and mice and ten of squirrels. Some of these undoubtedly take other foods, but all are essentially herbivores. Forty-five large herbivores occur, including thirty-seven species of antelope and their relatives. With the exception of four species of pig (which take some animal food), all are herbivores. There are ninety-one insectivores, of which fifty-six are bats and nineteen are shrews. Some, such as the pangolin which feeds upon termites, have a very restricted diet. The bats take nocturnal flying insects. There are forty-one essentially flesh-eating carnivores, but some (hyaenas, jackals) are in part scavengers from bigger carnivores, and some (mongooses and their relatives) eat insects and fruit as well as flesh, while otters eat fish, molluscs, and crabs. Eleven species of fruit bats eat fruit (including cultivated varieties) and pollen. Some of the ten species of monkeys are fruit-eaters, others eat leaves, and some, such as the baboon, are partly flesh-eaters. The chimpanzee is essentially a fruit-eater. Lastly, man is omnivorous, in some areas being dependent mainly upon fruit, vegetables, and seeds, in others on flesh and fish. It must be pointed out, however, that many mammals, particularly monkeys and the smaller carnivores, are opportunist in regard to feeding, and although they can be broadly classified allowance must be made for variation.

Apart from the smaller number of species, the mammal fauna of Britain differs from that of Tanganyika in the absence of antelopes and the presence of three species of deer, in the absence of

* Tanganyika and Zanzibar are politically united as Tanzania.

essentially tropical mammals such as monkeys, fruit bats, pan-golins, aardvark, mole-rats, hyraxes, and of the large herbivores (such as hippopotamus, rhinoceros, elephant, and giraffe) and of large carnivores and mongooses, and in the presence of two species of seal. One should note, however, that large herbivores and carnivores have in the past million years been common and widespread in the north temperate region, including Britain.

The abundance of insects and fruit and the year-round avail-ability of vegetable food (especially grass) probably accounts for the greater number of species in Tanganyika than in Britain. Past history is also important: Tanganyika has had a relatively stable environment for a much longer time than Britain, and of course Tanganyika is part of a vast continent and Britain is now an island. The absence of seals from the Tanganyika coast (and other tropical coasts) is peculiar, but large shoals of fish (which in turn are associated with abundant plankton) upon which seals feed are less frequent. In Britain, earthworms contribute enormously to the diet of some carnivores and insectivores. Earthworms are scarce in tropical Africa and no mammal could be dependent on them for food; the place of earthworms is probably taken by termites, which are eaten by several species of mammals in Tanganyika.

2. *The Breeding Birds of Kenya and of France and Switzerland*

About 802 species of land birds breed in Kenya, whereas about 241 species breed in the combined area of France and Switzerland. These species are distributed among seventy-three families in Kenya and fifty in France and Switzerland. Thirty families found in Kenya do not occur in France or Switzerland, including guinea fowls, parrots, turacos, wood-hoopoes, hornbills, barbets, honey-guides, cuckoo shrikes, bulbuls, and sunbirds, to mention only the larger families. Seven families that occur in France and Switzer-land do not occur in Kenya, but each contains relatively few species: these are grouse, oystercatchers, nuthatches, dippers, treecreepers, wrens, and accentors. Some of the families that occur in both areas are poorly represented in France and Switzer-land: the weavers, including sparrows, are one such family.

There are, then, about three and a half times as many species of birds in Kenya as in France and Switzerland. What can be said to characterise the bird fauna of Kenya, a large and variable tropical area, as compared with that of France and Switzerland, a large and variable temperate area? In Table 1 are listed some of the families of birds that contain a total of ten or more species in the two areas combined. These families are selected in an attempt to demonstrate the difference in the bird fauna of the two areas.

TABLE 1 The number of species in some of the larger families of birds found in Kenya and in France and Switzerland.

	Kenya	France and Switz.		Kenya	France and Switz.
		Estimated number of species:			
herons	12	7	kingfishers	10	1
ducks and geese	14	13	hornbills	12	—
birds of prey and vultures	40	17	barbets	19	—
			woodpeckers	12	8
game birds	17	5	swallows	13	4
rails and crakes	14	7	crows	4	9
pigeons and doves	15	5	titmice	7	8
turacos	10	—	bulbuls	23	—
cuckoos	14	2	warblers	64	27
owls	12	8	flycatchers	34	3
nightjars	11	2	shrikes	32	4
swifts	11	3	sunbirds	32	—

Birds that are mainly predators of vertebrates are better represented in Kenya. Thus herons, birds of prey, owls, and kingfishers are represented by two to three times as many species. Many of the kingfishers of Kenya are terrestrial feeders, taking large insects and small vertebrates, but there are also some fish-eating species. Many of the birds of prey are scavengers and feed chiefly on dead mammals. Fruit- and seed-eaters, such as pigeons and turacos, are represented by five times as many species in Kenya. Predators of large insects, such as shrikes, have about eight times as many species, and sunbirds, which are nectar-feeders and have thirty-two species in Kenya, do not occur in France or Switzerland. There are many more species of birds in Kenya that feed upon winged insects; these include swifts, nightjars, swallows, flycatchers, and many of the warblers, but caterpillar- and nut-feeders, such as titmice, are less well represented. Ducks and geese are equally represented in the two areas; many are herbivores and some are grazers. Crows are omnivores, but in

France and Switzerland the species are at least partly dependent upon earthworms and caterpillars; earthworms are rare in the lowland tropics of Africa, and there are less than half as many species of crows in Kenya as in France and Switzerland. Woodpeckers are a puzzling group; one might have expected a great many species in the forests of Kenya. They are not replaced by any other group of birds, and their scarcity (in number of individuals as well as in species) is possibly due to most of the trees having smooth bark and being less likely to harbour insects in large numbers; this is in marked contrast to the trees of temperate Europe, many of which have rough bark which harbours many insects. Game birds are largely herbivorous, and the larger species (not including guinea fowl) are better represented in France and Switzerland.

Kenya, then, differs from France and Switzerland in having many more predatory and insectivorous birds, more nectar- and fruit-eating birds, but fewer woodpeckers and species that eat earthworms.

But comparisons such as this involve many practical difficulties. Kenya and France and Switzerland have been considerably altered by man, but France and Switzerland more so than Kenya. The effect of man on the bird fauna is to make many habitats unsuitable for certain species while other species flourish. Another difficulty is that of making comparisons. Is it possible that grazing birds are in Kenya to some extent replaced by grazing mammals, and woodpeckers by predatory insects? Lastly, many of the species that breed in France and Switzerland spend only half the year there. Many such species migrate and spend the northern winter in Africa, including Kenya. The effect of this annual influx of northern migrants on the species-composition of the resident bird fauna is unknown.

3. *Lycaenid Butterflies in Uganda and Britain*

Lycaenid butterflies are small or medium-sized insects with a rapid flight; many are brightly coloured. In an area of mixed oak wood and chalk grassland in Britain it would be possible to find twelve species. In the Mpanga Forest of Uganda seventy-eight species have been recorded (Jackson, 1961) and there are probably others that have not yet been collected. About sixty-eight species of butterflies occur in Britain, and hence there are more lycaenid butterflies in the Mpanga Forest than there are species of butterfly in the whole of Britain. In Britain several species of lycaenid are dependent in their early stages upon a symbiotic relationship with ants. Many of the Mpanga species are probably also associated with ants, and the enormous number of species may be partly because of the large number and variety of ants.

The Abundance of Species

Birds, mammals and lycaenid butterflies are better represented in terms of number of species in tropical Africa than in the north temperate regions. A similar trend occurs in almost every other group of animals. Does this increased number of species affect the abundance of each species?

It is often maintained that relative to those of the temperate regions tropical species are rare. Some temperate and especially arctic species of animals are extremely abundant, and populations of small mammals and other groups often reach plague proportions at high latitudes. But unfortunately because of lack of information it is not possible to make more than a subjective comparison of the numbers of temperate and tropical animals: there are very few estimates of the numbers of each species in tropical habitats.

It is evident, however, that not all tropical species are rare. Some of the large ungulates of the East African savanna are extremely abundant, probably as abundant as equivalent species at high latitudes. The African thrush, *Turdus pelios*, is a common bird in gardens in East Africa, essentially occupying the niche of the blackbird, *Turdus merula*, in Europe, and gives the impression of being as abundant as the European blackbird. Many species of African butterflies, beetles, and grasshoppers, and some species of land snails, for instance *Limicolaria* spp., are locally at least as abundant as any European species.

It would be possible in tropical Africa to make a complete census of all the species of certain groups, such as birds, in a selected small area, and to compare the results with censuses of comparable species that have been made in the temperate regions. Until this is done no positive statement about the relative abundance of tropical African species can be made.

Even though abundant species in tropical Africa may be as

abundant as comparable species in the temperate regions, there seems little doubt that there are many more rare species in the tropics. Thus each of several species of earthworms is on the whole rare in the lowland tropics of Africa, while the species found in the temperate regions are often very abundant; many species of African grasshoppers are also relatively rare. Hall and Moreau (1962) in a study of the rare birds of Africa south of the Sahara conclude that there are more species that rank as rare than in North America, Europe, the temperate parts of Asia, and Australia. They list ninety-six species of birds that have a range of less than 250 miles in any direction or that are known by very few specimens. Most of these rare species are confined to isolated mountain forest, especially in Angola, Kenya, and Tanganyika. The warblers and the sunbirds include the highest percentage of rare species. No comparison is made with tropical Asia and tropical America, and it is not known whether Africa has more rare birds than the other tropical areas of the world.

Tentatively, then, it can be concluded that a feature of tropical Africa (and presumably other tropical regions of the world) is a large number of relatively rare species of animals. On the other hand some common species may be as common as comparable species in the temperate regions. It may well be that the essential difference between tropical and temperate regions is the increased number of rare tropical species and not the decreased number of common species, and that this in turn is a corollary of the fact that there are more species.

The Diversity of Tropical African Species of Animals

A. R. Wallace repeatedly drew attention to the greater number of peculiar and unusual species of animals found in the tropical regions of the world. Tropical representatives of many widely different animal groups differ fundamentally in structure from their closest relatives, and some are highly specialised in their way of life. Some examples, chosen from different groups of animals, serve to illustrate the point.

Mammals are world-wide, and in all the major tropical areas of the world there are mammals that feed mainly upon ants and termites. The pangolins, *Manis* spp., of Africa and tropical Asia are the sole representatives of a distinct mammalian order, the

Pholidota. They feed on termites and to a lesser extent on ants and have many modifications in structure associated with this specialised diet. Fig. 4 shows the general appearance of an African pangolin. It has no teeth, the snout is long and there is a long tongue. The front feet have powerful claws for digging, and the eyes are small. Horny overlapping scales cover most of the body.

Fig. 4. Two diverse mammals of tropical Africa. Above, a pangolin, *Manis* sp., and below, an aardvark, *Orycteropus afer*. These mammals are termite-eaters, and have many structural modifications associated with this way of life. (Redrawn in part from Bere, 1962.)

Pangolins are nocturnal and some climb trees, but little is known of their ecology or numbers, except that they are inconspicuous and eat termites and ants. Pangolins are very different from any other mammals.

Another ant- and termite-eater, the aardvark or ant-bear, *Orycteropus afer*, is the sole representative of the order Tubulidentata. It is confined to Africa, although fossil evidence suggests that aardvarks once had a much wider distribution in Europe and Asia. As shown in Fig. 4, it has a long snout, a small mouth, but, unlike pangolins, does not have scales. It has a long tongue and a few peg-like cheek teeth. Aardvarks feed at night, spending the day in a hole in or near a termite mound, but again little is known of their ecology. They may be the only survivors of a much bigger order of mammals, which may even have ranged as far as North America.

The fossil records of birds are considerably less informative than those of mammals and little is known of the past distribution and relationships of some of the strikingly diverse African species.

One of these, the whale-headed stork, *Balaeniceps rex*, is placed in a family by itself, the Balaenicipitidae. The whale-headed stork is quite rare and is hardly ever

FIG. 5. An unusual tropical African bird, the whale-headed stork, *Balaeniceps rex*. The function of its remarkable bill is not known.

seen unless a special search is made. It inhabits papyrus swamps in Uganda, the southern Sudan, and the Congo, and looks like a large heron but, as shown in Fig. 5, its bill is enormous and shaped like a shoe. Like many herons and some storks it feeds upon fish, including lung-fish, and amphibians, but nothing is known of the function of the remarkable bill, which is unparalleled in any other species of bird.

The honeyguides, Indicatoridae, are a family of birds that occur in tropical Asia as well as Africa. They are forest species, and frequently make themselves conspicuous by their behaviour and voice, thus attracting mammals, including man, to bees' nests. The mammal then destroys the nest for its honey and the honeyguide feeds on pieces of beeswax that are left scattered around. Apart from this remarkable behaviour, honeyguides are unusual in that they are among the few vertebrates that can digest quantities of wax.

Tropical Africa has many diverse and unusual invertebrates. There is a caddis fly, *Limnoecetis tanganicae* (order Trichoptera), that as an adult skates over the surface of the water like a pond-skater (Hemiptera) or a whirlygig beetle (Coleoptera). It is confined to Lake Tanganyika, and was first described as recently as 1955. The species is illustrated in Fig. 6, where it can be seen that it bears a strong resemblance to a bug rather than to a caddis. Then there is a reduviid bug, *Acanthaspis petax*, the nymphs of which decorate themselves with particles of soil and the corpses of their prey, especially ants. The bug lives on large termite mounds, and in East Africa one can often see what appears to be a cluster of dead ants moving quickly over the surface of these mounds. The larvae of a fruitfly, *Leucophenga* sp. (Drosophilidae), live in the masses of spittle formed by nymphs of the cercopid bug, *Ptyelus flavescens*, an unusual niche for fruitfly larvae (Odhiambo, 1958). In the East African lakes there is a woodboring mayfly (Ephemeroptera) nymph; this species, *Povilla adusta*, has powerful mandibles associated with wood-boring, but it is a filter-feeder and does not eat wood.

Jellyfish are usually associated with the sea, but some species occur in fresh water: in the East African lakes the medusae of *Limnocnida* spp. are sometimes found in large swarms; the hydroids are attached to the stems of aquatic plants. In the oxygen-deficient swamps of tropical Africa there is an oligochaete worm, *Alma emini*, which possesses an external longitudinal groove on the dorsal surface of the hind end. This structure is a respiratory organ, and occurs in other worms that live in oxygen-deficient swamps, especially in South America (Beadle, 1933).

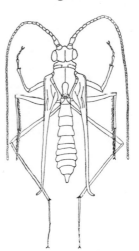

And so one could go on: many other examples of diverse tropical African animals could be cited. There are, perhaps, two kinds of diversity in animals.

FIG. 6. The water-skating caddis, *Limnoecetis tanganicae*, of Lake Tanganyika. (From Marlier, 1955.)

There are unusual species, like pangolins, that are anatomically distinct, exploit a restricted food source, and are therefore confined to relatively small areas. And then there are animals like the fruitfly just mentioned that have unusual ways of life, yet belong to widely distributed groups of animals. Diverse species present a challenge to the ecologist, and few tropical African examples have been studied in detail.

CHAPTER 3

Populations

The word population is from the Latin word *populus*, meaning people. Until relatively recently, discussion of populations was limited to human numbers. The word population is now used by ecologists to mean a number of organisms of a single species living in a particular place at a particular time. The chief aim of the population ecologist is to find out what determines the kinds and numbers of organisms in different areas at different times. The size of populations potentially increases geometrically. Normally this does not happen. Most populations are stable, and the problem is to find out what environmental factors determine stability. The problem of the potential growth and of the regulation of animal populations is of fundamental importance: human numbers are unstable and the world population of man is increasing by about sixty-five million a year. No other animal of even remotely comparable size and distribution is in this position. By understanding the means by which animal numbers are regulated, and by considering the complexities of adjustment to the environment, one may perhaps begin to understand human population problems. A consideration of human numbers is no less important in tropical Africa than in other parts of the world.

The Distribution of Populations of Species

If one takes a map of Africa and plots on it the distribution of a species of animal, a distinct pattern emerges. If one repeats the exercise for a number of different species, it becomes apparent that some species have a wide and continuous distribution while others are extremely restricted.

The turacos are birds that are confined to Africa. There are eighteen species and most of them have a restricted distribution.

Fig. 7 shows the distribution of two species, the Ruwenzori turaco, *Tauraco johnstoni*, and the great blue turaco, *Corytheola cristata*. *Tauraco johnstoni* occurs in highland forest on Ruwenzori, the highlands north-east of Lake Edward, the Kivu volcanoes, the highlands north-west of Lake Tanganyika, and nowhere else. It is confined to highland forest and has a very restricted range. In

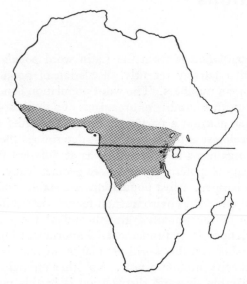

FIG. 7.   The distribution of two species of turaco in tropical Africa. The small isolated black areas indicate the distribution of *Tauraco johnstoni*, the large shaded area the distribution of *Corytheola cristata*.

contrast *Corytheola cristata* ranges from Guinea and Fernando Po in the west right across equatorial Africa to western Kenya. It occurs as far north as 9° 40′ N. in Nigeria and south to about 11° S. in Angola. It is a bird of lowland forest and forest edge, and also occurs in savanna where there are plenty of trees. The wide distribution of this species can be compared with the restricted distribution of the related *Tauraco johnstoni*: one species is found throughout the lowland equatorial belt while the other is confined to highland forest. It is clear that the distribution of these two types of habitat determines the distribution of the birds; but this is a descriptive statement and tells nothing of the means by

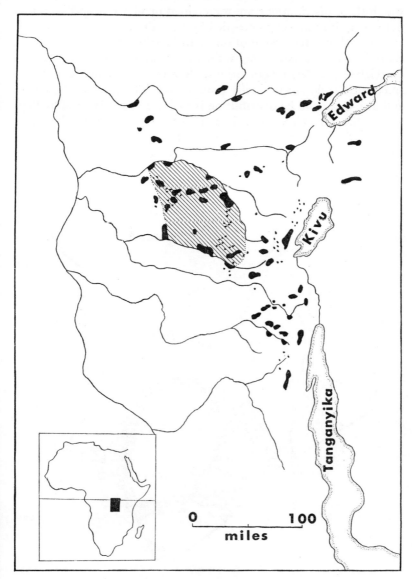

FIG. 8. The distribution of the mountain gorilla, *Gorilla gorilla*, in central Africa. The black areas are isolated populations and the shaded area indicates a probably continuous distribution. (From Schaller, 1963.)

which these distributions are maintained or why one species does not spread into the area occupied by the other.

Fig. 8 shows the distribution of the gorilla, *Gorilla gorilla*, in central Africa. As can be seen, the species occurs in many isolated or relatively isolated populations. Rivers form a major barrier since gorillas do not normally cross them. The gorilla is a stem- and pith-eater and its distribution is to some extent limited by the availability of suitable food. In some areas it is persecuted by man and its range has decreased, but in others it has increased as it exploits some of the crops grown by man. There is at the moment

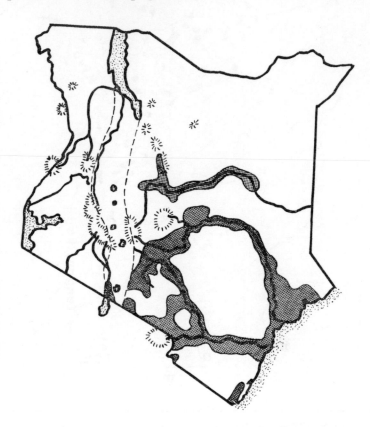

FIG. 9. The distribution of the waterbuck, *Kobus ellipsi-prymnus*, in Kenya. Major mountains are shown, and the dotted lines indicate the position of the Rift Valley. (From Stewart and Stewart, 1963.)

no danger of gorillas becoming extinct, but their numbers may decline rapidly if human numbers continue to rise.

Fig. 9 shows the present distribution of the waterbuck, *Kobus ellipsiprymnus*, in Kenya. It occurs chiefly along river valleys and in low-lying country. This pattern of distribution is found in many other animals that live in seasonally dry parts of tropical

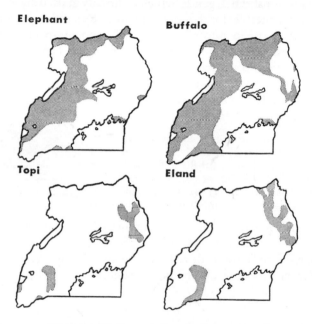

FIG. 10. The distribution of the elephant, *Loxodonta africana*; buffalo, *Syncerus caffer*; topi, *Damaliscus korrigum*; and eland, *Taurotragus oryx*, in Uganda.

Africa. West of the Rift Valley the place of *Kobus ellipsiprymnus* is taken by a similar species, *Kobus defassa*, and it too is closely associated with river valleys. The ranges of the two species overlap where they meet.

Fig. 10 shows the present distribution of the elephant, *Loxodonta africana*; buffalo, *Syncerus caffer*; topi, *Damaliscus korrigum*; and eland, *Taurotragus oryx*, in Uganda. Judged by distribution, the general ecological requirements of the elephant and the buffalo are similar, as are those of the topi and eland. The elephant and the buffalo occur where there are at least some trees and in particular where seasonal drought is less marked; the topi and the eland can tolerate more open and drier country. Fig. 11 shows the areas of Uganda where the mean annual rainfall is above and below forty inches. The association of the elephant and the buffalo with areas of higher rainfall and the topi and the eland with areas of lower rainfall is conspicuous, except near Lake Victoria in southern Uganda which is heavily settled by man and is hence unsuitable for large mammals. But although such an association between rainfall and distribution of species of large mammals exists, little is known of the ecological factors that limit the distribution in this way.

Figs. 7–10 show that species have characteristic distributions. Some species are obviously restricted by features

FIG. 11. The areas of Uganda where the mean annual rainfall is above (shaded) and below (unshaded) forty inches. The distributions of the large mammals shown in Fig. 10 seem to be associated with this rainfall pattern.

of the environment such as mountains, rivers, forests, and the amount of rainfall. But so far the problem of numbers has not been considered: these distribution maps simply show whether a species is present or absent in a particular area.

Dispersion

The word dispersion is here used to denote not only where a particular animal is found but also how many there are in a limited area. Animals are not randomly spaced: there is generally a well-defined pattern in frequency in a given area. This frequency-pattern is what is meant by dispersion. The simplest example of non-random dispersion of a species is in man. Man is most abundant, and towns and villages are larger, in areas where resources and means of communication are best. The availability of food, shelter, the relative freedom from predators and parasites, and a favourable climate are the kinds of environmental factors that determine the dispersion of a given population. Two examples of dispersion in populations of tropical African animals, one a land snail, the other a bird, will be considered.

In tropical East Africa, the herbivorous land snail, *Limicolaria martensiana*, occurs in well-defined populations separated from each other by ecological and geographical barriers. The snails are three to four centimetres long when they are adult, and where they occur they are conspicuous. Table 2 shows the dispersion of Population A at Kampala, Uganda. The figures shown are the number of snails in a metre frame quadrat (1·2 square yards) taken at regular intervals throughout the population. The population occupies an area of thirty thousand square metres. The number of snails in each quadrat varies from none to 202. It is clear that the dispersion of snails in the population is not even and it can be shown to be non-random. Snails become progressively more frequent from north to south, and also from east to west. The twenty-five foot contours are shown diagrammatically in Table 2. Between the lowest two contours there are 46·7 snails per quadrat, while between the middle two contours there are 10·7 snails per quadrat. Above the highest contour snails are rare: only one out of nine quadrats contained a snail. The slope of the land, and particularly the presence of a small stream on the west side of the population, results in the south-west corner being damp and the north-east corner relatively dry. The gradient in wetness from north-east to south-west accounts for the dispersion of snails in this population. Other factors may also be involved, such as the availability of food.

In another population (Population B) of the same species, the dispersion of the snails depends to some extent upon the occurrence of a particular food-plant. Population B covers an area of 3,450 square metres; there is no noticeable slope and evidently no moisture gradient. The population was sampled in the same way as Population A. The results for two series of samples on two dates are shown in Table 3. The pattern of dispersion is similar, indicating stability. The snails are relatively rare in the north and north-west, and rather rare in the south-east; they are concentrated about the middle. The solid lines in Table 3 indicate the area within which a favoured food-plant, *Bryophyllum pinnatum*, covers more than fifty per cent of the ground. The association of increased numbers of snails with a greater amount of *Bryophyllum pinnatum* is not spectacular (the snails eat a wide variety of other plants), but dispersion is clearly related to the abundance of this one food-plant.

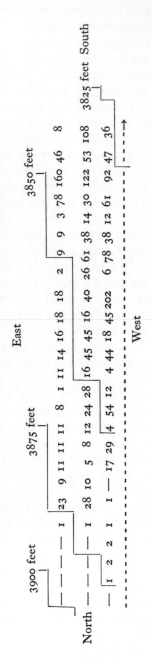

TABLE 2 Dispersion of the land snail, *Limicolaria martensiana*, in Population A at Kampala between 14th February and 13th March 1963. Each figure represents the number of living snails in a metre quadrat taken in the south-west corner of a twenty-metre square. The solid lines show the approximate position of the twenty-five foot contours. The dotted line indicates the position and direction of flow of a small stream.

TABLE 3 Dispersion of the land snail, *Limicolaria martensiana*, in Population B at Kampala on 10th April 1963 and 5th November 1963. Each figure represents the number of living snails in a metre quadrat taken in the north-east corner of a twenty metre square. The solid lines indicate the area within which the food-plant, *Bryophyllum pinnatum*, covers fifty per cent or more of the ground.

10th April 1963

East

1	3	19	27	8	12
2	24	22	39	115	17
—	4	7	16	32	28

North ... South

West

The mean density inside the solid line is 30·5 per square metre; outside it is 8·9 per square metre.

5th November 1963

East

—	8	11	27	16	7
5	33	33	58	63	4
1	22	28	25	52	48

North ... South

West

The mean density inside the solid line is 35·9 per square metre; outside it is 10·3 per square metre.

It is thus clear that dispersion within these two populations of *Limicolaria martensiana* is neither random nor even, but is related to environmental factors, including a moisture gradient and the abundance of a particular food-plant. Land snails are sedentary animals and presumably patterns of dispersion such as these are rigidly fixed and are maintained for long periods.

The fish eagle, *Cuncuma (Haliaëtus) vocifer*, is a large and conspicuous bird in tropical Africa. It feeds upon lake and river fish, catching its own prey and scavenging around fishing villages. Fish eagles tend to be spaced at intervals along the shores of lakes and rivers. In 1962 a census was made of the fish eagles along the eastern shore of Lake Albert (Green, 1964). About 209 kilometres (130 miles) of shore was examined and 167 fish eagles were counted; this gives an average of 0·8 eagles per kilometre. The dispersion of the fish eagles and the position of fishing villages is shown in Fig. 12. The dispersion of the eagles appears to be determined by

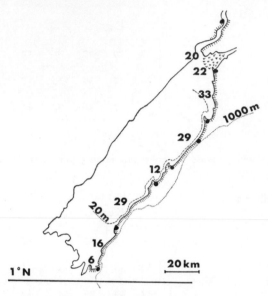

FIG. 12.   The dispersion of the fish eagle, *Cuncuma* (*Haliaë-tus*) *vocifer*, along the eastern shore of Lake Albert, Uganda. The thousand-metre contour marking the edge of the Western Rift Valley and the twenty-metre depth line are shown. Solid dots mark the position of fishing villages. Where the Nile enters and leaves the Lake at its northern end, there are extensive papyrus swamps. The shoreline censused is shown by hatching. (From Green, 1964.)

three factors. First, fish eagles use conspicuous perches with a wide view of the lake. These are usually dead trees at the edge of the water. Fish eagles are relatively rare where perches are scarce, as along the southern section of the shore where the escarpment of the Rift Valley plunges steeply into the Lake. Secondly, they are frequent where the water is shallow and fish more available. Where the Nile enters the northern part of the Lake there are extensive papyrus swamps and here fish eagles are numerous.

Thirdly, numbers are higher around fishing villages, partly because the birds are able to scavenge, and partly because, like fishermen, eagles tend to concentrate where fish are most available. Hence the dispersion of the fish eagle on the shores of Lake Albert is not random or even, but is determined in a variety of ways. It is important to note that suitable food must not only be abundant but that it should also be available. It appears that fish eagles and fishermen share an interest: both are more concentrated where resources are more available.

Dispersion and Behaviour

There are in many species behavioural mechanisms by which individuals become dispersed. Many species of birds and fish, some mammals and insects, and some other animals isolate themselves from others of their species at the time of breeding. Many of these species are territorial; a 'territory' is an area that is defended against other members of the same species. One outcome of territorial behaviour is that individuals acquire for themselves a private space within which they can live and breed. In many birds and fish territories are defended only in the breeding season; outside the breeding season they may be social and gregarious. The ecological result of territories is that animals are spaced out, and hence resources, which may include food and a suitable place to breed, are better utilised. The establishment of a territory also increases the probability of obtaining a mate: males of many species make themselves conspicuous by their territorial behaviour and so attract suitable females into the territory.

In birds, territorial behaviour is somewhat less conspicuous in tropical than in temperate species. This is because many tropical species remain in the same area all their lives whereas most temperate species breed in areas other than those in which they spend the rest of the year. Temperate species thus have to re-establish themselves in their breeding territories each time they breed; this is not so in many tropical species, especially those living in the lowland forest with its seasonally unchanging environment. Cichlid fish, however, congregate in the breeding grounds in and around the East African lakes and each male establishes a territory which it defends against other males of the same species (Lowe, 1956).

One of the common antelopes, the kob, *Adenota kob*, is in parts of Uganda territorial all the year round (Buechner, 1961). Small territories are defended within a larger area of concentrated territorial activity; this area is surrounded by a zone of more widely spaced territories. Females may enter the defended area at any time of the year for the purpose of mating. This particular type of territorial behaviour does not appear to have been observed in other tropical mammals, and seems associated with high population density.

Social species may also be dispersed in such a way as to utilise the available resources most effectively. Colonies of social birds such as weavers, and colonies of termites, are spaced out in such a way as to ensure effective utilisation of food and other resources. Some species of weavers breed in colonies in villages occupied by man or in trees occupied by large predators such as eagles; this pattern of dispersion would appear to afford the colony some degree of protection from enemies. In some animals, for example social wasps and hunting dogs, there is a division of labour within the social group. The wasps have a worker caste that assist in the feeding of the larvae and in the care of the nest. In the hunting dog, *Lycaon pictus*, all the adults are equally qualified for hunting and for guarding and feeding the young, but at any one time only a few of the adults take part in a hunt; the others remain behind and take care of the young. The meat is brought back by the hunters and is shared among the guards and the young (Kühme, 1965).

Population Size and Population Density

Finding out the distribution of species and the dispersion of individuals and populations is the first step in any attempt to evaluate the factors that limit the size of populations. The next step is to find out the size and density of populations.

As pointed out in Chapter 2, some tropical African species are common and many are relatively rare, but apart from the large mammals of the East African savanna very few estimates of population size and density of tropical African animals are available. This is chiefly because of the great practical difficulties involved in obtaining such estimates. Two general methods are available: direct counting and sampling. Direct counting is effective if the animals are large and conspicuous (the large mammals of the savanna can be counted with relative ease) or if the animals are sedentary. Sampling can be effective for animals that are relatively small and that do not move around too much: populations of land snails and soil invertebrates can be readily sampled and reliable estimates of population size and density can be obtained. Most populations of flying animals (bats, birds, and adult insects) are difficult to estimate, and nocturnal and aquatic species present special problems. I do not intend to discuss here the many

TABLE 4 Numbers, population density, and biomass of some large herbivorous mammals on the Rwindi-Rutshuru Plain, Eastern Congo. The figures are the means of six counts made in 1959. From Bourlière (1963).

Species	Average adult weight in kg	Number in 600 square km	Density per square km	Biomass per square km, in kg
elephant, Loxodonta africana	3,000	1,026	1·7	5,100
hippopotamus, Hippopotamus amphibius	1,400	4,800	8	11,200
buffalo, Syncerus caffer	500	7,402	12·3	6,150
topi, Damaliscus korrigum	130	1,199	2·0	260
waterbuck, Kobus defassa	150	760	1·2	195
Uganda kob, Adenota kob	70	4,976	8·3	581
warthog, Phacochoerus aethiopicus	70	603	1	70

Note: About five other species of large herbivores also occur, but they are relatively rare. No figures are available for small mammals, primates, and carnivores.

sampling methods available for different groups of animals, neither shall I discuss the difficulties that can be encountered. These methods and their associated difficulties are the same in the tropics as in the temperate regions; a good account of sampling methods in population ecology is given by MacFadyen (1963).

Bourlière (1963) has summarised some of the estimates of population size and density of large mammals, chiefly herbivores, that have been made in the East and Central African savanna, and to a lesser extent elsewhere. Some of the large herbivores may have very high population densities, especially in areas that have been set aside as national parks.

Table 4 shows the number of large herbivores in the Rwindi-

Rutshuru Plain of the Eastern Congo; the average weight of each species and the biomass per square kilometre is also given. Biomass is calculated by multiplying the average weight by the density: it is a useful measure of the 'amount' of each species in a given area. The combined biomass of large herbivores on the Rwindi-Rutshuru Plain, 23,556 kilograms (51,920 pounds) per square kilometre, is probably the highest figure for any natural area in the world. About sixty-nine per cent of the biomass is

TABLE 5 Numbers, population density, and biomass of ungulates and primates in the Tano Nimri Forest Reserve, Ghana, in 1954. From Bourlière (1963).

Species	Average adult weight in kg	Number in 250 square km	Density per square km	Biomass per square km, in kg
duiker, Philantomba maxwelli	8	79	0·31	2·48
duiker, Cephalophus dorsalis	20	38	0·15	3
antelope, Neotragus pygmaeus	4	7	0·03	0·12
black colobus, Colobus polykomos	10	916	3·6	36
red colobus, Colobus badius	8	621	2·4	19
diana monkey, Cercopithecus diana	5	144	0·57	2·8
mona monkey, Cercopithecus mona	5	127	0·50	2·5
mangabey, Cercocebus torquatus	8	83	0·33	2·6
olive colobus, Colobus verus	4	5	0·02	0·08
chimpanzee, Pan troglodytes	40	22	0·09	3·6

made up of two species, the elephant, Loxodonta africana and the hippopotamus, Hippopotamus amphibius. Many comparable estimates are available for other savanna areas in East and Central Africa. Table 5 gives some estimates of numbers, density, and biomass in an area of West African forest. The combined biomass of the three species of ungulates is only 5·6 kilograms per square kilometre. Diurnal primates (monkeys and the chimpanzee) are the most conspicuous mammals of the West African forests, but the seven species listed in Table 5 comprise only 66·6 kilograms per square kilometre. Some of the forests of the Congo and

Uganda support large populations of elephant and buffalo, but no reliable estimates of numbers are available. In general, large mammals are much scarcer in the forest than in the savanna,

TABLE 6 Number of pairs of large birds of prey in 146 square miles in the Embu District of Kenya. From Brown (1955).

Species	Number of pairs		
	1950	1951	1952
secretary bird, *Sagittarius serpentarius*	4–5	1	—
Verreaux's eagle, *Aquila verreauxii*	1	1	1
Wahlberg's eagle, *Aquila wahlbergi*	8	9	11
African hawk-eagle, *Hieraaetus spilogaster*	2	2	2
Ayres' hawk-eagle, *Hieraaetus ayresi*	1	1	1
martial eagle, *Polemaetus bellicosus*	3	3	3
crowned hawk-eagle, *Stephanoaetus coronatus*	1	1	1
long-crested hawk-eagle, *Lophoaetus occipitalis*	1	1	1
bateleur, *Terathopius ecaudatus*	2	2	2
brown harrier-eagle, *Circaetus cinereus*	2	2	1
black-breasted harrier-eagle, *Circaetus pectoralis*	1	—	—
fish eagle, *Cuncuma vocifer*	1–2	2	2

Not every pair nested successfully.

chiefly because grass is scarce in heavy forest, and the largest ungulates feed mainly on grass.

If however all animals were considered, including insects and other invertebrates, the biomass of the forest animals would be considerably higher, though certainly never as high as the savanna. On the other hand there is little doubt that the forest supports a much greater number of species than the savanna, but no overall comparison is available because of lack of information: most forest animals are relatively small, whereas some savanna species are very large. It can be said with certainty that the African savanna supports a much greater biomass of animals than any comparable temperate area.

Some of the drier areas in East Africa support large numbers of birds of prey. Up to twelve species of eagle and eagle-like birds can occur together. Table 6 shows the results of a census of large birds of prey made during three consecutive years in the Embu district of Kenya (Brown, 1955). The area includes rocky hills, heavily bushed river valleys, and wooded savanna. Apart from the fish eagles, which feed upon fish, and the secretary bird, which feeds upon grasshoppers as well as vertebrate prey, all the species are predators of small- or medium-sized mammals, large passerine birds, game birds (including domestic chickens), lizards, and snakes. A large number of prey species have been recorded as being eaten by the eagles, but possibly they are mainly dependent on a few species, such as hyraxes, game birds, and certain snakes and lizards. As shown in Table 6, with the exception of the secretary bird, *Sagittarius serpentarius*, numbers remained stable in each of the three years. This suggests a close adjustment between the eagles and their available prey.

Little information is available on the population size and density of tropical African invertebrates. As discussed in Chapter 2, many species seem relatively rare, but some are extremely abundant locally. The arthropod fauna of the soil appears to include only about half as many individuals in tropical African pasture as in English pasture (Salt, 1952). There may be over fifty thousand arthropods to the square yard in the top six inches of soil in parts of tropical Africa, but about twice that number in English soils. Unfortunately little is known of the species-composition of the arthropod fauna in tropical African soils. Undoubtedly some species, particularly ants and termites, are extremely abundant, and probably have densities exceeding thousands per square yard. On the bottom of freshwater lakes the immature stages of some species of aquatic insects may occur locally at densities of thousands per square yard, and sometimes there are very large concentrations beneath suitably positioned stones. In the swamps of Uganda, Cladocera (small freshwater Crustacea) of different species may occur at densities of between 5 and 320 per litre of water (Thomas, 1961). These figures are subject to much variation in different parts of the same swamp, but seem about the same as densities obtained for Cladocera in the English Lake District.

The above are a few examples of the order of magnitude of population size and density for a few groups of tropical African animals. There is in fact comparatively little numerical information of this sort on animal populations in tropical Africa. Much routine counting and sampling is needed, especially of invertebrates, and this could be achieved by teams of students from schools and colleges as class exercises.

Parasites and Hosts

Parasites occur on and in most animals. By definition parasites do not normally kill their hosts, but they may occasionally have severe effects and may sometimes cause the death of the host. Both the size of parasite populations and the density of parasites in hosts present peculiar problems.

If a large sample of hosts is examined and the frequency of a particular species of parasite on each is recorded, it is often found that most of the parasites are associated with relatively few of the hosts. Table 7 shows the numbers of a parasitic crustacean, *Argulus africanus*, found on a large sample of the fish, *Tilapia esculenta*, in a tropical African lake. There is a mean of 3·18 parasites per host, but over half the parasites are on only eight per cent of the fish. Thus a few fish are very heavily parasitised and most fish are lightly parasitised. This kind of distribution of

TABLE 7 The frequency of a parasitic crustacean on a fish. From Williams (1964).

Parasites per fish	Number of fish	Parasites per fish	Number of fish
0	154	14	3
1	70	15	2
2	25	16	1
3	22	17	3
4	6	18	4
5	8	19	3
6	4	20	3
7	8	21	2
8	3	22	2
9	1	24	2
11	4	28	2
12	7	30	1
13	1	34	1

parasites on hosts can be shown to be neither random nor even. Similarly, in a sample of 560 specimens of the Lake Nyasa fish, *Bagrus meridionalis*, 333 were infected with the parasitic crustacean, *Lernaea bagri*. Again, most of the fish were lightly infected but a few were heavily infected (Fryer, 1956).

There is as yet no satisfactory explanation of this non-random occurrence of parasites in hosts. D. J. Bradley informs me that the frequency of *Schistosoma* in man shows a similar pattern: in parts of tropical Africa most people are infected, but few suffer seriously from the disease; serious effects from schistosomes are the result of large numbers of the parasite. It is clear that, besides being of ecological interest, this non-random occurrence of parasites in hosts may have important medical implications: one might expect that in diseases caused by parasites relatively few people would suffer very serious effects even though most people may be infected.

Factors Limiting Populations

The population size and density of a species vary in different environments, and species differ markedly in abundance. With this information, it is now necessary to consider the ways in which populations are regulated.

In general, populations may be regulated in two ways: by density-dependent or by density-independent events. Density-dependent events are environmental factors that operate differently at different population densities. In particular, the mortality-rate increases with increasing population density and decreases with decreasing population density. The availability of food and the pressure exerted by predators seem to act density-dependently on most populations, but this does not mean that food availability and predator pressure always act in this way, even in the same population. Density-dependent events are not easy to detect in the field, but there is some direct and much suggestive evidence of their action. Density-independent events are environmental factors whose effect is not related to the density of the population. Density-independent mortality seems to occur when there is a sudden environmental change that affects all members of the population equally. A grass fire could kill all members of a snail or an insect population no matter what the population density. A rise in water level could also kill density-independently. Plate IV shows the effect of the recent rise in the level of Lake Victoria: trees around the edge are killed off by the water, and this mortality is independent of the density of the trees. It may be assumed that any sedentary animals on the living trees would also die density-independently.

Density-dependent events tend to maintain a population at

PLATE III. An elephant feeding on a bush in the savanna. Elephants feed chiefly on grass and similar plants, but at times supplement their diet with the leaves and stems of bushes and trees. (Photograph by C. H. F. Rowell.)

PLATE IV.   Forest trees that have been killed by the rising level of the water in Lake Victoria, January 1965. This and other tropical African lakes are subject to irregular fluctuations in the level of the water, partly because of variations in rainfall and partly because of human activities such as dam building and drainage projects. The mortality of the trees and the animals associated with them is probably density-independent, as discussed in Chapter 3. (Photograph by C. H. F. Rowell.)

relative stability at a certain level which depends upon the particular environment. Fluctuations are relatively small because whenever numbers tend to become too high the mortality-rate increases. The size and density of a given population depends upon the resources available to it; such resources include the availability of food, shelter, breeding places, and so on. Density-independent events, on the other hand, tend to produce large fluctuations in numbers and occasional extermination of the population. In a survey of factors that limit populations in temperate animals, especially birds, Lack (1954) concluded that density-dependent events operate in most populations and that density-independent events are rarely important. It is likely, however, that many populations are at least occasionally subject to density-independent regulation.

If then most populations are limited primarily by density-dependent events, it follows that as numbers tend to rise there must be competition for resources among individuals. Competition is likely whenever animals share the same controlling factors; that is to say, when there are not enough resources available, some individuals die while others survive. There is much indirect and some direct evidence that competition for food is the chief limiting factor for many animal populations. It is likely that most populations of predatory animals (including the many predatory insects) are food-limited, and hence there is competition among predators for the available prey. On the other hand one has the impression that many herbivorous animals have an unlimited supply of green plants; but appearances may be deceptive. Animals that depend upon fruits and flowers may be just as liable to food-shortage as those that feed on other animals. In the evergreen forests of tropical Africa it is not easy to see how leaf-eating species can ever be short of food, since the forests seem always green and most of the leaves are not eaten; but on the other hand many leaves are tough and may be unpalatable.

In my garden at Kampala there is a small citrus tree. Swallowtail butterflies, *Papilio demodocus* and *Papilio dardanus*, often lay their eggs on the new leaves: evidently the young larvae cannot eat the old tough leaves. Young swallowtail larvae therefore depend upon the availability of young leaves; most of the leaves on the citrus are unacceptable. But as the larvae grow, they are able to eat older leaves, and yet despite the abundance of food hardly ever attain full growth. They are subject to intensive predation by mantids and other insects. If they are brought indoors and reared on leaves gathered from the same tree they usually attain full growth. Hence it seems that these swallowtails may be limited as young larvae by the availability of young leaves, but that later they are limited by predators.

In the savanna there is periodic drought, and although most of the time there may be plenty of available plant food there may also be times of food scarcity. In some of the savanna areas of East and Central Africa that have been set aside as national parks, elephants, *Loxodonta africana*, are extremely abundant. In the vicinity of the Murchison Falls National Park in Uganda, eighty-eight per cent of the total food in a sample of seventy-one elephants was grass (Buss, 1961). Around Murchison, the availability of grass varies seasonally: during the dry season grass becomes relatively scarce, partly because of intensive burning by man. At this time elephants also destroy trees and bushes, and into such destroyed areas grass rapidly spreads; it is possible then for fire to spread in and destroy more trees. Under such circumstances forests can be replaced by savanna. With the regular alternation of wet and dry seasons, grassland becomes more and more dominant relative to woodland. Hence because they tend to destroy the woody part of their habitat elephants in the long run provide more grass for themselves. The situation here described has never been properly analysed, but there is evidence that with protection elephants are limited by the availability of grass in the dry season. In areas where they are protected they tend to increase and their tree-destroying activities prompt the growth of grass, which in turn provides more food. The numbers of elephants may thus be limited by seasonal grass in a density-dependent way.

The open-billed stork, *Anastomus lamelligerus*, feeds mainly on the large amphibious snail, *Pila ovata*. This snail becomes abundant in wallows formed by the hippopotamus, especially if, as is often the case, the water cabbage, *Pistia stratiotes*, becomes the dominant plant of the wallows. The size of a wallow depends upon its age and upon the number of hippopotamuses using it. Big wallows can be completely choked by *Pistia*, which in turn supports a large population of *Pila*. The storks become concentrated at wallows and feed on the snails, often using the back of a wallowing hippopotamus as a perch from which they can catch the snails. The number of storks at any particular wallow seems to depend on the number of snails, which in turn may depend on the amount of *Pistia*, which itself depends upon the hippopotamus creating the wallow in the first place. It is possible, though by no means certain, that the storks are density-dependently food-limited while the snails in the wallows are limited not by *Pistia*, which is very abundant, but by density-dependent predation by the storks. This interpretation is based upon qualitative observations, and the whole situation should be analysed quantitatively.

Tsetse flies, *Glossina* spp., feed as adults on the blood of large mammals, especially ungulates. They are never very common even in areas where there are large concentrations of mammals. Various workers have speculated that the population size of tsetse is controlled by factors such as climate, and some have suggested that the control acts density-independently. The argument is that large mammals supply potential food far in excess of that required by the number of flies actually found. But there are two reasons for thinking that tsetse are in fact food-limited in a density-dependent manner. First, the flies seem highly selective in the species of mammals from which they take blood. Table 8 shows the relative abundance of large mammals in an area of East Africa and the nature of the gut contents of flies collected in the same area. In this area the most abundant mammal, the impala, *Aepyceros melampus*, contributed only one per cent of the food of the flies, while the warthog, *Phacochoerus aethiopicus*, which was relatively scarce, contributed seventy-seven per cent. Only one buffalo, *Syncerus caffer*, was found in the area, yet buffalo blood was found in fourteen per cent of the flies. It is evident from Table 8 that not all of the available mammals are utilised by the flies, but why this should be so is not known since the blood of the different species is nutritionally similar. The preferred food of the flies is relatively scarce. Secondly, there is much evidence that as the density of biting flies (including tsetse) rises, mammals scratch and shake themselves more frequently. This may result in the flies being unable to feed properly, and hence their numbers may be limited by decreased availability of blood as the result of the behaviour of the mammals. Both the analysis of the fly gut contents and observations on mammal behaviour illustrate the importance of food-availability rather than food abundance; it appears that superficial impressions of a great amount of food may be misleading, and that abundant food is not necessarily always available.

TABLE 8 Relative abundance of large mammals and the food of *Glossina swynnertoni*. From Glasgow (1963).

Species of mammal	Frequency of mammals (per cent)	Presence of mammal blood in gut of flies (per cent)
warthog, *Phacochoerus aethiopicus*	2·68	77
rhinoceros, *Diceros bicornis*	0·21	2
buffalo, *Syncerus caffer*	0·02	14
dikdik, *Rhynchotragus* sp.	7·89	—
Grant's gazelle, *Gazella granti*	2·61	—
giraffe, *Giraffa camelopardalis*	6·63	—
hartebeest, *Alcelaphus* sp.	3·51	—
impala, *Aepyceros melampus*	69·91	1
lesser kudu, *Strepsiceros imberbis*	0·68	—
waterbuck, *Kobus* sp.	4·38	—
other large herbivores	0·46	—
carnivores	1·01	—
Unidentified Bovidae		6
	99·99	100

Note: The percentage frequency of mammals is based upon a mean of 180 mammals seen daily during the scanning of about two square miles. 139 fly meals were examined.

The level of oxygen in some tropical swamps is low. This is the result of the abundance of plant material and a corresponding increase in oxygen-consuming micro-organisms. Oxygen-depletion is accelerated by high temperatures, limited movement of the water, and relatively little photosynthesis because of shading from light. The density of oxygen-consuming micro-organisms determines the level of oxygen and they are therefore competing for oxygen among themselves. Whether this results in competition for oxygen in other (metazoan) animals of the swamps is not known, but the possibility exists (Beadle, 1961).

The above examples are strongly suggestive of the widespread importance of density-dependent events and competition in the regulation of animal numbers in tropical Africa. As already mentioned, density-independent events, such as grass fires and rising levels of water, also act on many populations, but their effect has been even less precisely analysed than the density-dependent events just discussed.

Reproduction- and Death-rates

Many tropical passerine birds lay smaller clutches of eggs than similar species in temperate regions. Clutches of two eggs are common among tropical passerines; comparable species in the temperate regions lay five or six eggs. In general, the reproduction-rate of birds depends upon the availability of food to the young at the time of breeding. At high latitudes the food available to young birds is greater during a limited time than in the tropics; the hours of daylight are longer during the time that the birds breed and there is often a sharp peak in abundance of food at this time. In the tropics sharp peaks of food rarely occur, and at any one time there is less food available than during the peak of availability in the temperate regions. It seems likely therefore that the low clutch-size of tropical passerines is an adaptation to limited food-availability. There is little evidence that the clutch-size is an adjustment to the death-rate; both the reproduction-rate and the death-rate seem to be independently adjusted to the available resources, in particular to the availability of food.

The problem of the evolution of reproduction-rates in birds and in other animals has been discussed at length by Lack (1954). His general conclusion is that reproduction-rates are a product of natural selection and are as efficient as possible: numbers of animals are not in general controlled by variations in reproduction-rates, but by variations in death-rates, usually acting density-dependently. In tropical Africa there is much scope for investigation of reproduction- and death-rates in relation to availability of resources; this is virtually an untapped field of research.

Population Density and Body Size of Animals

Growth inhibition as the result of overcrowding is well known in laboratory populations of aquatic snails, tadpoles, and other aquatic animals. These animals evidently release a growth-inhibiting substance which has a marked effect on other members of the population. Larger individuals release relatively more of the substance and suppress growth in smaller individuals. *Biomphalaria sudanica*, an aquatic snail in tropical Africa, releases a substance which appears to inhibit growth in other snails in the same population (Berrie and Visser, 1963). This has been demonstrated in natural populations, and if the phenomenon is of widespread occurrence in this species it is clearly important in the regulation of populations, if, as in many animals, maturation occurs only when growth has reached a certain point. Such a mechanism may exist in many other species of aquatic animals and could be of considerable importance in regulating population density. The mechanism of growth inhibition clearly acts density-dependently, but a similar effect could occur without the actual release of a particular substance. Populations of fish at high density tend to contain many individuals that are smaller than average, particularly if food is scarce, but here reproduction is often independent of growth and population size is not affected.

Food shortage affects adult size in a great many species of insects. The effect is best seen in species whose larvae are gregarious; such larvae sometimes completely defoliate the plant upon which they are feeding, but instead of dying they pupate early and produce small adults. Some natural populations of insects show great variation in adult size, for example mantispids (Neuroptera). In a single population of these insects there may be individuals that are twice the size of others of the same sex. Immature mantispids feed on young spiders within their cocoons. This is a specialised method of feeding, and it may be that because spider cocoons vary in size, food may not be equally available to all mantispids and that this results in the marked variation in adult size.

Body size, then, may in some cases be indicative of the operation of density-dependent events within populations acting either directly through a shortage of resources (usually food) or indirectly by the release of growth-inhibiting substances.

Ecological Segregation

If competition is important in determining the size of animal populations, one would expect mechanisms to evolve that would tend to reduce the effects of competition. Ecologists since Darwin have repeatedly drawn attention to the fact that similar species of animals usually differ in their ecological requirements. In any group of related species it is usually possible to find differences in morphology that in general reflect differences in ecology, especially in the kind of food eaten or the particular part of the habitat from which the food is obtained. Such ecological segregation between species is thought to be an evolutionary product of interspecific competition for limited resources: if species tend to have different ecological requirements, competition will be less intense. Many examples of ecological segregation are known from tropical African animals. Morcau (1948) examined ecological differences in 172 species of birds living in an area of three thousand square miles in Tanganyika. He found that ninety-four per cent of the related species (species in the same genus) differ in diet or in habitat or in both. This analysis excluded the weaver birds, the species of which show greater similarity than other birds. Most weavers feed on temporarily superabundant grass seeds, and in the dry season when the seeds become scarce the weavers move to other areas of temporary superabundance.

There are in Africa two species of *Schistosoma* that cause bilharzia in man. These endoparasites are of great medical importance. One species, *Schistosoma haematobium*, depends upon aquatic snails of the family Bulinidae for its intermediate hosts. These snails are most abundant in the drier areas of Africa and they are able to resist temporary drying up of their habitat; hence *Schistosoma haematobium* is especially associated with the drier areas of Africa. *Schistosoma mansoni* on the other hand depends upon snails of the family Planorbidae for its intermediate hosts. These snails are most abundant in the wetter parts of equatorial Africa. Thus the two species of *Schistosoma* associated with man are ecologically segregated by habitat and by the intermediate host they use. But there is further ecological segregation in the two species: *Schistosoma haematobium* is associated with the human bladder, while *Schistosoma mansoni* is associated with the intestine. The two parasites thus derive their food from different parts of the human body. It is possible for an individual man to be infected with both species, but generally this is not so because of the different habitats occupied by the intermediate hosts.

Species of birds and of schistosomes are ecologically segregated. Such segregation between species is of such widespread occurrence that its significance in reducing competition seems certain.

Concluding Remarks on Animal Populations in Tropical Africa

A feature of population regulation in tropical Africa and presumably in other tropical areas of the world is that the factors controlling a given population are in many cases highly complex. Many more species occur within a single area than in the temperate regions; many species take many different foods and are preyed upon by a large variety of predators. Simple predator-prey situations, which have been repeatedly analysed in the temperate regions, seem rare. Few cases of population regulation have so far been analysed quantitatively and most of what has been said in this chapter is of a highly descriptive nature; there is much scope for detailed investigation, and a start could be made with relatively simple examples, such as the hippo-snail-stork association already described. Density-dependent events would appear to be of greatest importance in population regulation, but the possibility exists that density-independent events are relatively more important in the tropics than in the temperate regions; the presumed density-independent effects of fires in the grassy areas of Africa may prove to be of widespread importance in the regulation of many animal populations. Tropical African populations seem relatively more stable than temperate populations. Cyclic fluctuations in numbers are unknown, and one has the impression of an extremely complex environment that imparts considerable long-term stability.

CHAPTER 4

The Seasons
and other Periodic Events

In the temperate regions, most biological phenomena are seasonal. In Britain, for instance, birds breed chiefly in April, May, and June; each species of butterfly flies at only a certain time of the year; many invertebrates and some vertebrates hibernate; and many insects and birds migrate, arriving from the south in the spring and departing for the south in the autumn. These events are regular and predictable: if an insect flies as an adult in a particular month in one year it will normally do so every year.

Such regular seasonal events are obviously adapted to the occurrence of a clearly defined winter and summer, and a somewhat less clearly defined spring and autumn. The main environmental factors that determine seasonal biological events in temperate regions are incremental changes in daylength and changes in air temperature. Changes in daylength are absolutely regular and predictable, and it is therefore not surprising that a great many animals, particularly birds and insects, respond readily to such changes. Temperature fluctuations, although regular, are not absolutely predictable; everyone living in the temperate regions is familiar with the occasional mild or very cold winter.

A visitor from the temperate regions is perhaps at first surprised to find that in the tropics, even near the Equator where seasonal changes in daylength and temperature are small, most animals have a seasonal rhythm in many of their activities. In the lowland tropics the seasons are less obvious to the casual observer, for a number of different reasons. First, especially in forested regions, the habitat looks uniformly green all the year round. Secondly, whereas in temperate regions a whole group of animals (such as birds) may be more or less synchronised in such activities as breeding and migrating, in the tropics they are not. In Britain most birds breed in the spring, but in a tropical country such as Uganda birds may be found breeding in all months of the year, although for a particular species breeding may be restricted to a relatively short period. Thirdly, for reasons that follow, many seasonal events that occur once a year in the temperate regions occur twice a year in the tropics.

In the tropical regions of the world, including tropical Africa, there are more or less predictable seasonal changes in the amount of rainfall. In general most tropical areas enjoy two relatively wet and two relatively dry seasons in a year. The word 'relatively' is important, because in many regions, especially in the equatorial forest region of Africa, rain falls all the year round, and it is only by careful measurement over several years that a seasonal pattern emerges. In the absence of marked changes in daylength and temperature it is not surprising that in tropical Africa most seasonal events are associated directly or indirectly with seasonal fluctuations in the rains. In the temperate regions, rainfall may on occasion modify the effects of changing daylength and temperature, but in the tropics the situation is reversed: temperature and daylength may on occasion modify the effects of rain.

Proximate and Ultimate Factors

In discussing seasonal and other rhythmic events, it is convenient to distinguish two kinds of factors that are important in maintaining the rhythm. These may be referred to as proximate and ultimate factors. Proximate factors are environmental events that serve as a trigger to an animal's physiology; they convey to the animal information about the time of year, time of day, likelihood of food shortage, and so on. The many ways in which proximate factors operate present problems for the environmental physiologist rather than for the ecologist. Proximate factors in general stimulate a rhythm but are not themselves the ecological reason for the rhythm; their general effect is to synchronise events for a given population. Ultimate factors, on the other hand, are events that determine why an animal breeds, migrates, moults, aestivates, and so on, at a particular time. Ultimate factors present problems for the ecologist and evolutionist rather than for the physiologist. In general, ultimate factors are periodic environmental events that make resources more available for a particular population at certain times than at others. Here is a classification of some proximate and ultimate factors that are of importance to animals in tropical Africa:

Proximate factors (or how the animal knows when to respond): changing length of day; fluctuation in air temperature; seasonal rainfall; variations in relative humidity; diurnal fluctuations in amount of illumination; the phases of the moon.

Ultimate factors (or why the animal responds at a particular time): availability of food; availability of breeding site; absence or comparative rarity of predators and parasites; synchronisation of appearance of breeding adults; seasonal availability of water and humid conditions; seasonal fires and seasonal drought.

A proximate factor can under certain conditions also act as an ultimate factor. Thus, seasonal rainfall can stimulate breeding proximately and at the same time can be the ultimate reason for breeding at a particular time; a decreasing food supply could act as the proximate and the ultimate stimulus for an animal to move from one place to another. Very often, though, the proximate and ultimate factors controlling the occurrence of a biological rhythm are different. Thus in Africa seasonal rainfall often acts as a proximate stimulus for birds to breed, but the ultimate factor is increased availability of food.

Exogenous and Endogenous Rhythms

Most biological rhythms in animals appear to be stimulated by environmental events acting in the first place through the nervous and hormonal system. Environmentally determined rhythms are usually known as exogenous. But there are also rhythmic events that cannot be easily correlated with environmental stimuli, and it is postulated in such cases that there is a rhythm within the animal itself; this is called an endogenous rhythm. It is difficult at present to say how widespread endogenous rhythms are, because although it is possible to show that exogenous rhythms occur it is impossible to show that they do not occur. Hence, to postulate that there is an endogenous rhythm, it is first of all necessary to eliminate the possibility of occurrence of external events, an extremely difficult task. In some well-investigated examples it appears that exogenous and endogenous rhythms can combine. Near the Equator, where changes in daylength and temperature are small, it is tempting to suppose the endogenous rhythms are relatively more important than in temperate regions. Whether this is so remains to be investigated. My impression is that the flowering pattern of many plants at Kampala is such that endogenous rhythms may be involved. The flowering pattern of a single iris plant, *Marica caerulea*, in my garden at Kampala is perhaps suggestive of an endogenous rhythm. The flowers of this plant last only one day, and flowering is cyclic. Several flowers (once there were fifty-two) appear on one day and then there are no flowers for an interval of a few days. During 105 consecutive days in 1964, a mean of 3·5 flowers occurred once every 3·1 days. Hence the flowering of this plant is neither random nor seasonal, nor does it appear to be associated with any climatic or other external factor. It is possible, then, that in this plant there is an endogenous rhythm the overall effect of which is to synchronise periodic flowering.

The development of a bright yellow breeding plumage in a small passerine bird, the yellow wagtail, *Motacilla flava*, just before departure from its equatorial 'wintering' grounds for the breeding grounds in northern Europe and Asia has been cited as an example of an endogenous rhythm (Marshall and Williams, 1959). These birds, along with many other migratory species, leave their breeding grounds in Europe and Asia in late summer and autumn under the proximate stimulus of decreasing daylength. They migrate to equatorial Africa, arriving in late September, and depart again for the north in March and April. Around Entebbe, Uganda in January many of the birds begin to develop the bright yellow plumage associated with the breeding season. Entebbe is 0° 04′ N. and changes in daylength are negligible; temperature fluctuations are irregular and slight, and in every month more than 2·5 inches of rain falls. Marshall and Williams (1959) claim that there is no seasonal change in the supply of insect food, and postulate because of this that an endogenous rhythm is at least partly responsible for the development of bright plumage in January before the return migratory flight. In fact there is ample evidence of considerable fluctuations in the numbers of most species of insects near the Equator, but whether this is enough to create a periodic shortage of food for the yellow wagtail and so induce departure for the north is not known.

Hence, although it is tempting to postulate endogenous rhythms among equatorial animals, the evidence for them is not convincing. I am inclined to the view that some plants may have endogenous rhythms and that some animals have developed an exogenous response to these plants.

The Seasons at Kampala

Kampala, at 0° 20' N., is almost on the Equator. There are about twelve hours of daylight and twelve hours of darkness all the year round. The mean maximum temperature is around 80° F. and the mean minimum is 60° F. Fluctuations in temperature in each twenty-four hour period are greater than seasonal changes. There is virtually no seasonal change in temperature: January and February are on the average a few degrees warmer than June and July, but the effects are not obvious. Minimum temperatures normally occur at night and maximum in the afternoon. Once or twice a month, after heavy rain, the temperature may fall as low as 55° F. The Kampala sky is rarely completely clear, and it is often very cloudy, especially in the afternoon. Thunderstorms are frequent in the early afternoon or during the early hours of the morning, and usually come from Lake Victoria to the south. Some storms may be accompanied by hail and high winds, which cause considerable damage to crops. Prolonged light rain may occur in the normally wetter months of April and November, but most of the rain falls during thunderstorms. The vegetation is generally lush all the year round, and superficially one has the impression that most animals are performing most of their activities regardless of the time of year. Many animals, especially insects and birds, are responsive to rainfall, and activities may start or stop with the onset of rain. The monthly rainfall at Kampala for the ten years 1953–62 is shown in Table 9. During this period the total annual rainfall varied between 35 and 64 inches, with a mean of 46. The mean monthly rainfall is always in excess of two inches and never over seven inches, July being on average the driest month and April the wettest. On average there are two relatively wetter seasons, March-April and October-November, and two relatively drier seasons, January-February and June-July. But the means are deceptive, as shown in Table 9. The wettest month of the year may come earlier or later than usual

AE E

TABLE 9 Monthly rainfall at Kampala, Uganda, 1953–62. Kampala is at 0° 20′ N. (Figures supplied by the East African Meteorological Department, Entebbe.)

Year	Jan.	Feb.	Mar.	Apr.	May	June	July	Aug.	Sept.	Oct.	Nov.	Dec.	Total for year
1953	2·77	1·84	1·79	4·98	2·77	5·94	0·72	3·43	5·31	7·31	4·46	2·04	43·36
1954	0·32	2·67	2·10	2·53	5·75	2·30	4·95	3·37	3·74	2·69	0·89	3·73	35·04
1955	3·40	5·54	6·31	7·92	5·31	2·21	3·04	6·72	4·64	2·11	2·37	3·91	53·56
1956	4·03	0·62	2·51	9·46	2·29	0·91	0·52	3·74	1·87	2·14	5·41	3·71	37·21
1957	3·52	1·71	8·02	8·34	0·73	2·85	1·89	2·88	1·43	2·27	3·58	5·48	42·70
1958	1·70	2·60	6·18	6·65	3·71	2·74	2·94	3·44	4·60	2·91	3·58	5·01	46·06
1959	1·84	1·50	3·26	4·67	1·66	0·78	1·60	7·08	3·93	3·83	8·19	3·34	41·68
1960	5·11	2·03	6·91	9·30	6·90	1·86	1·93	2·37	4·48	4·01	2·06	1·24	48·20
1961	0·00	1·62	9·01	7·27	5·00	1·69	1·90	5·77	4·93	12·77	9·93	4·52	64·41
1962	2·41	0·92	8·58	7·30	3·31	2·78	0·65	4·84	3·47	7·61	4·60	4·74	51·21
Mean	2·51	2·10	5·47	6·84	3·74	2·41	2·01	4·36	3·84	4·77	4·51	3·77	46·34

in any particular year, and sometimes, as in 1954, a normally dry month (July) may be wet while a normally wet month (November) may be dry. Many animals living in the Kampala area show some seasonal periodicity in their activities, and in most cases rainfall appears to be the most important proximate factor. For instance, every time there is heavy rain or even the likelihood of heavy rain, a small bird, the white-browed robin-chat, *Cossypha heuglini*, bursts into melodious song. This bird rarely sings unless it rains. Mole crickets, *Gryllotalpa*, also sing after rain, whereas during dry spells they are hardly ever heard. Winged termites and ants take flight soon after rain. The biological activity of many animals around Kampala is strongly influenced by rain, far more so than by any other single environmental event.

Breeding Seasons of Animals in Tropical Africa

Birds are the only major group of animals in tropical Africa for which there is a reasonably complete picture of breeding seasons. For most species rainfall appears to be the most important proximate stimulus to breed. In East Africa, away from the influence of the large lakes, there are two relatively well-defined rainy seasons in the year, and breeding tends to occur twice a year, either in the dry seasons or in the wet seasons, depending upon the species. The most important ultimate factor affecting the breeding seasons of birds appears to be seasonal availability of food for the young, but few species have been studied in detail from this point of view. In the more humid climate of the Congo and also in the forested regions of West Africa, many species of birds seem non-seasonal. Chapin (1932) has discussed in general terms the breeding seasons of birds in the lowland equatorial forest of the Congo. Here rainfall is well distributed and temperature fluctuations are small. The breeding activity of passerine birds is less in the drier months of November–January, but there are many species that are exceptions: woodpeckers breed especially in November–January, and doves and birds of prey tend to avoid the wetter months of February–May. It is, however, possible that there are seasonal peaks in activity even in areas of equatorial Africa where birds of a particular species breed in every month of the year. For instance a colony of black-headed herons, *Ardea melanocephala*, at Nairobi, Kenya was occupied by breeding herons in every month for the four years 1958–62, and there is evidence that a colony of this species has been used continuously for twenty years at Kampala (North, 1963). But although the black-headed herons at Nairobi breed continuously, their activity varies; in particular, the number of birds breeding declines during dry weather and increases with the rains.

The breeding seasons of mammals are not as well documented as those of birds, although there is at present considerable interest, especially in ungulates. In the savanna an important ultimate factor for ungulates may be the appearance of new vegetation, especially grass, after the rains, and climatic variation may be, as in birds, the most important proximate factor. The availability, during and after the rains, of long grass in which new-born young can hide may also be important. Some carnivores appear to breed when their chief prey species are themselves giving birth to young. Many mammals in tropical Africa appear to breed all the year round, but in the few instances where large samples have been examined distinct peaks in breeding activity have been found. Information on breeding seasons is almost non-existent for the forest species, and surprisingly little is known about the primates.

Kellas (1955) examined a sample of 412 specimens of a small antelope, *Rhynchotragus kirkii*, collected at Shinyanga, Tanganyika (3° 33′ S.). Females were found to be polyoestrus throughout the year, with two periods of intensive breeding, one at the beginning of the rains in November and one at the end in April. The gestation period in this species lasts about six months, and

most females become pregnant twice a year. Spermatozoa occur
in adult males at all times of the year, but the testes, epididymides,
and seminal vesicles show a seasonal fluctuation in weight that
corresponds with the breeding cycle of the females. Young born
at the beginning of the rains are able to enjoy the cool long-grass
season, while those born at the end of the rains spend their first
few months of life in hot, dry weather during which the vegetation
becomes progressively more and more sparse. The two seasons
into which the young are born are hence very different, but both
lots of young are dropped when the grass is long; this, then, may
be the most important ultimate factor.

In Uganda the elephant, *Loxodonta africana*, breeds all the year
round, but there is possibly a seasonal peak (Perry, 1953); the
difficulty is in obtaining a large enough sample.

There is at the moment an increasing interest in the biology of
the large ungulates of the East African savanna, and it is to be
hoped that much information on breeding seasons will soon become available.

What little information there is for the primates suggests that
many species breed all the year round. The red-tailed monkey,
Cercopithecus ascanius (nictitans), appears seasonal in Uganda, as
shown by the following records collected by Haddow (1952):

Period	Per cent in early pregnancy	Per cent in late pregnancy	Per cent with infants
January–April	19	—	31
May–August	4	36	—
September–December	—	9	18

The sample of fifty-two upon which these are based is admittedly a
small one, but there appears to be a peak in breeding activity in
December-April. Other species of *Cercopithecus*, and also *Colobus*,
and baboons, *Papio* spp., may be non-seasonal (Haddow, 1952).
Man also appears to be non-seasonal in breeding.

Mutere (1965) has found that in the fruit bat, *Eidolon helvum*,
living near the Equator at Kampala, not only is breeding strongly
seasonal but there is also delayed implantation. The young are
born in February and March. The weight of the testes varies
seasonally, reaching a peak in April–June, when also spermatozoa
are most abundant. Spermatozoa are found in the genital tracts
of the females only during April–June, but implanted embryos do

not occur until October. During July–September unimplanted blastocysts are present in the uterus, and there is hence a delay of about three months between fertilisation and implantation. This appears to be the first record of delayed implantation in a tropical mammal and in a bat; delayed implantation has until now been known only from mammals in temperate regions. In *Eidolon helvum* the ecological significance of delayed implantation, and indeed of seasonal breeding, is obscure; the bats feed largely upon cultivated fruits which do not appear to vary in abundance seasonally.

In Gambia the West African lung-fish, *Protopterus annectens*, aestivates when seasonal drying up of the swamps commences in November and December. Lung-fish remain in aestivation for seven or eight months until the rains, and then, once the swamps are flooded, they begin to breed. Breeding is thus strongly seasonal, and may be earlier or later in any particular year, depending upon the condition of the swamps (Johnels and Svensson, 1954). Less is known about the breeding of the East African lung-fish, *Protopterus aethiopicus*: in Uganda breeding occurs chiefly in November–April and, as in *Protopterus annectens*, is associated with higher rainfall; unseasonal breeding may occur if there are unseasonal rains (Greenwood, 1958).

In Lake Nyasa the rock-frequenting cichlid fish seem to breed all the year round (Fryer, 1959). In northern Lake Victoria the cichlid, *Tilapia variabilis*, also breeds all the year round, but with peaks at somewhat irregular intervals, especially in November and December and in July (Fryer, 1961). The seasonal breeding patterns of lake and river fish in tropical Africa pose a number of interesting questions; a great many deep water species move into shallower water for spawning, but the proximate factors stimulating this movement are obscure. Anadromesis, or up-river migration, occurs in a number of species. At certain times of the year (especially during the rains) large numbers of several species of Cyprinidae and Clariidae migrate up-river from Lake Victoria. Breeding then takes place in the swampy upper reaches of the rivers. Little is known of either the proximate or the ultimate factors involved in anadromesis; rising water levels seem important, and it is thought that the migration ensures better feeding grounds for the young fish and reduces the chance of predation from large lake fish.

The entire activity, including breeding, of tropical African frogs and toads is much influenced by rain. Like birds, many frogs begin to sing soon after rain has fallen, and often frog spawn may be found in temporary puddles formed after a downpour. Many of the smaller forest species breed in seasonal water holes in trees.

In most areas the Nile crocodile, *Crocodilus niloticus*, lays its eggs during the dry season, and hatching occurs with the onset of the rains. In Uganda the crocodile occurs in the Nile, and from Lake Kyoga northwards breeding takes place once a year in December and January. But to the south, in northern Lake Victoria, breeding occurs twice a year: in August and September and in December and January (Cott, 1931). In other parts of Africa there is evidence that crocodiles lay when the weather is dry and the young appear with the rains. In Ghana the largely insectivorous rainbow lizard, *Agama agama*, breeds when the weather is wet, possibly because this is when food is most abundant (Chapman and Chapman, 1964).

Although there is ample evidence that invertebrates vary in abundance seasonally, there is very little documentation of seasonal breeding. Seasonal fluctuations in numbers are, of course, strongly suggestive of seasonal breeding.

Fig. 13 shows the seasonal pattern of breeding in the land snail, *Limicolaria martensiana*, at Kampala. Weekly samples of snails were collected from a single population from November 1962 until October 1963. After collection the snails were removed from their shells and the number of eggs recorded. The upper histogram in Fig. 13 shows the percentage of adult snails with eggs collected in each month. The snails lay eggs all the year round, but there are two peaks, one in February and the other in July: these peaks correspond with the normally drier months of the year. The actual monthly rainfall during the period of collection is shown in the lower histogram in Fig. 13. The seasonal pattern of breeding found in *Limicolaria martensiana* would result in many newly-hatched snails feeding during the normally wettest months of the year when suitable vegetation for food would be more available and when there would be less risk of desiccation. The alternation of relatively wet and relatively dry seasons could provide the proximate stimulus for fluctuations in breeding activity, and the chief ultimate factor is the increased general suitability of the habitat when it is wet. In the Western Rift of Uganda the same species of land snail is more seasonal in its breeding; this is presumably because the wet and dry seasons are much more sharply defined and regular. *Limicolaria martensiana*, then, resembles the

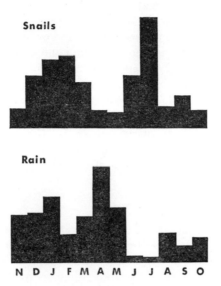

Snails

Rain

N D J F M A M J J A S O

FIG. 13.   The breeding season of the land snail, *Limicolaria martensiana*, at Kampala, Uganda. The upper histogram shows the percentage of adult snails with eggs in each month from November 1962 until October 1963. The peak of breeding occurred in July, when 33·1 per cent of the snails contained eggs; in May only 4·8 per cent contained eggs. The histogram is based on a sample of 5,381 snails, about 450 being examined in each month. The lower histogram shows the rainfall (in inches) at Kampala. April was the wettest month with 9·4 inches, and July the driest with 0·4 inches. Note that during this period the dry season was drier than usual and the wet season somewhat wetter (see Table 9). (From Owen, 1964.)

crocodile in its breeding pattern: both species lay most of their eggs at the end of the dry season in order to ensure that the young appear when it is wet.

Rainfall has a marked effect on the swarming pattern and seasonal colony formation of termites. New colonies of termites are founded by the simultaneous emission of winged reproductive males and females from established colonies. In many species the proximate stimulus for synchronised emission is rainfall after a dry spell. Often winged reproductives accumulate for a short time before setting out on their colonising flight. During this period the gonads are not fully mature and there is no sexual behaviour. Just before the flight from the colony, the worker termites make exit holes in the walls of the termite mound or burrow. Numerous workers and soldiers congregate around the exit holes when the reproductives fly off. Males and females leave the colonies in about equal numbers. They fly relatively short distances, mate and found new colonies. Many species of African termites are seasonal in their colony-founding flights, and most species are stimulated to fly by rainfall. Presumably rain is also the ultimate factor in termite flights: the ground would be softer and more suitable for starting a new mound or burrow after rain.

Migration and Seasonal Movements

Migration is a regular movement to and from a breeding area. In birds and other vertebrates, the same individual may take part in both movements; in most insects different individuals take part in the two movements. Migration, then, is a regular shift of a population from one place to another for the purpose of breeding.

Many birds that breed in temperate Europe and Asia spend the northern winter (September-March) in tropical Africa. Some Arctic species, including tiny warblers, migrate south, crossing Europe, the Mediterranean, and the Sahara to spend the northern winter in tropical Africa. Many of the migrants are insectivorous species such as warblers, flycatchers, swallows, and swifts; many others are birds that breed on tundra and moorland and migrate south to spend the winter around the shores of tropical lakes and ponds. The proximate stimulus for the departure of migrant birds for Africa is in many species decreasing daylength in the autumn, modified by decreasing air temperature. The chief ultimate factor is presumed to be decreasing availability of food, and perhaps also cold weather; but it must be emphasised that although there is much suggestive evidence for the operation of these factors, there is little direct evidence. An unanswered question is how the migrants in tropical Africa know when to return to the north. It is unlikely that on the Equator changes in daylength and temperature could act as proximate stimuli. Possibly there are seasonal changes in food availability in the tropics that act both proximately and ultimately.

It was at one time believed that northern birds reached tropical Africa by specific routes, the West coast and the Nile often being cited in this connection. But it is now known that many species

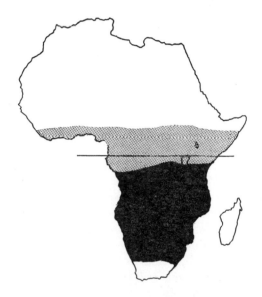

FIG. 14. The breeding area (solid black) and migration area (shaded) of the pennant-winged nightjar, *Semeiophorus vexillarius*. This bird has a wide breeding range south of the Equator and migrates north, but remains within the tropics during the southern 'winter'. Redrawn in part from Mackworth-Praed and Grant (1952).

can make a direct crossing of the Sahara, and that migration is often on a broad front and not along narrow routes.

Tropical Africa also receives migrants from South Africa and from Madagascar, and there are many species that migrate within the tropics. In general, the birds that breed in the equatorial forest are less migratory than those that breed in the savanna, presumably because seasonal climatic changes are less marked in the forest than in the savanna. The weaver birds are an abundant family in Africa, occurring both in the forest and in the savanna. Most forest species are non-migratory, but some savanna species undertake short-distance migrations. The pennant-winged night-jar, *Semeiophorus vexillarius*, is migratory within tropical Africa. The area in which it breeds and the area into which it migrates in the southern 'winter' are shown in Fig. 14.

In savanna areas where there is seasonal drought there may be considerable migrations of large mammals. The elephant and the wildebeest are mammals that in parts of their range in East Africa undergo regular migrations. Seasonal shortage of vegetation for food and of water are probably the ultimate factors involved in these movements.

Within tropical Africa, many insects are migratory, but little is known of the periodicity of the movements or of the ecological factors causing the movements. Butterflies of the families Pieridae and Nymphalidae have often been encountered moving in fixed directions, sometimes in immense numbers. In West Africa the butterfly, *Libythea labdaca*, migrates in a general southerly direction in February–May and in a general northerly direction in October–December (Williams, 1951). In the more humid parts of East Africa the long horn grasshopper, *Homorocoryphus nitidulus*, swarms at predictable times of the year. This species is closely associated with the rains of November and April, and in southern Uganda swarms normally occur in November and December and in April and May. *Homorocoryphus nitidulus* is nocturnal and is attracted in immense numbers to street lamps at night. It is extremely fat, a feature of many insects that migrate long distances.

Irruptions

Irruptions are irregular non-seasonal movements, usually caused by a failure of local resources, especially food, or by high population density, or by both. Irruptions are a feature of the less stable Arctic and sub-Arctic areas of the world: the periodic mass movements of certain rodents and birds at high latitudes are examples of irruptions.

In Africa, the desert locust, *Schistocerca gregaria*, is one of the most conspicuous animals that undergoes irregular mass movements. This species is a potential pest over nine million square miles of Africa and Asia, affecting about sixty countries. Within this area more than three hundred million people, one eighth of the world's population, are liable to suffer devastation of their crops.

Numbers of locusts may be so low for a number of years that it may even be difficult to find specimens for experimental work. Then there are sudden and unpredictable increases in local populations, followed by mass irruption. It is then that damage to crops occurs. The desert locust feeds on a wide variety of human crops and other plants, and can cause almost complete defoliation during an irruption. Swarms comprise up to a thousand million individuals and

FIG. 15. The area of Africa that is subject to mass irruptions of the desert locust, *Schistocerca gregaria*. From *The Hungry Thief*, published by Shell Limited (1956).

can consume three thousand tons of food a day. Fig. 15 is a map showing the area of Africa liable to invasion by the desert locust. At present, possibly because of control measures, it is exceptional for swarms to reach the equatorial parts of Africa, but parts of northern Kenya and the southern Sudan are likely to suffer periodically. The nymphs of the desert locust are green when not at high density, but as population density rises they become darker and take on a distinct yellow and black coloration. This transition, which is accompanied by many behavioural, physiological, and morphological changes, is referred to as the transition of phase *solitaria* to phase *gregaria*. There are many theories regarding the significance of phase transformation in this and other locusts, but despite an enormous amount of experimental and field study the function of the phases remains obscure. On one point there is no doubt: rising population density is the most important proximate stimulus for transition from *solitaria* to *gregaria*.

Irruptions have been discussed in this chapter because in many ways they can be considered to be a special kind of seasonal movement. They seem to occur in areas where normal seasonal stimuli break down or where populations become exceptionally large.

Aestivation

One way to avoid a seasonally unfavourable tropical environment is to move away from it; another way is to aestivate. Aestivation occurs in a number of invertebrates and in a few vertebrates that live in areas of tropical Africa that become seasonally or periodically dry. Species that live in shallow lakes or in swamps that dry up seasonally often survive the dry spell by aestivation in the mud, soil, or among vegetation. Three examples of aestivation from different groups of animals are discussed below.

During the dry season the Gambia River is restricted to its bed and the surrounding low-lying land is dry. During the rains this land is flooded and becomes a vast swamp, some of which is cultivated for rice. The onset of the rains, as well as the amount of rain, varies from one year to another, and this has an effect upon the aestivation cycles of a variety of species of animals, including the lung-fish, *Protopterus annectens*. Aestivation in this species has been studied by Johnels and Svensson (1954), from whom the account that follows has been taken. As the swamps dry up the lung-fish prepare themselves burrows in the mud. Unlike most fish that are found in the swamps during the rains, they do not move into the river when the dry weather sets in; in fact lung-fish are hardly ever seen in the river itself. The local name of the lung-fish is 'cambona', and when local fishermen are asked whether they catch cambona in the river, they reply, 'Cambona is not an ordinary fish. It does not follow the water but the water comes to cambona.' Fig. 16 shows the structure of the completed aestivation burrow of the lung-fish. At the surface of the swamp above the burrow there is an earth lid; below the lid is a tubular channel,

PLATE V. A 120-foot high steel tower erected in the Zika and Mpanga Forests in Uganda by the East African Virus Research Institute, Entebbe. There are platforms at regular intervals upon which insect traps have been placed. The tower has been extensively used to study insect flight activity at various levels in the forest (see Chapter 4). It has also provided information on biting and ovipositing cycles of flies of medical importance. The tower is an excellent place from which to watch the behaviour of monkeys and birds in the forest canopy. (Photograph by East African Common Services.)

PLATE VI. An irruption of the desert locust, *Schistocerca gregaria*. The picture shows part of a fifty square mile swarm over the airport at Hargeisa, Somali Republic, August 1960. Irruptions of this species are discussed in Chapter 4. The aircraft is one used by the Desert Locust Survey for spraying and destroying swarms of locusts. (Photograph by A. J. Wood, Desert Locust

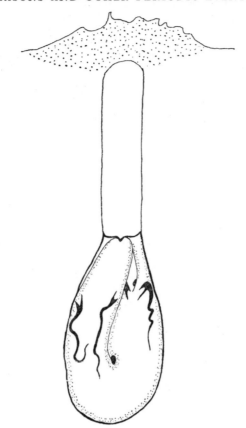

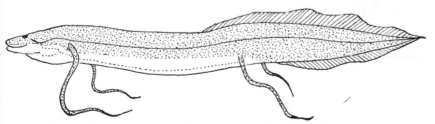

FIG. 16. An aestivation burrow of the lung-fish, *Protopterus anneetens*. The shaded area is the earth lid of the burrow. The fish is in position in its chamber at the base of the tubular part of the burrow. The lower figure is a lung-fish in the rainy season after aestivation. Partly from Johnels and Svensson (1954).

and finally there is the aestivating chamber of the lung-fish. The lung-fish fits tightly into this chamber and its normal position is shown in Fig. 16. Here it remains until the next rains. In some years the dry season is wetter than usual, and then many lung-fish do not complete the process of forming a proper aestivating chamber, but simply burrow into wet mud. The extent and length of the aestivation appears to depend entirely on the dryness of the season. The aestivating burrow of the East African lung-fish, *Protopterus aethiopicus*, is quite different from that of *Protopterus annectens*. It is a long chamber opening horizontally from a bank, and its base is filled with water (Wasawo, 1959). But very few aestivating chambers of *Protopterus aethiopicus* have been found and there may well be considerable variation in the mode of construction, depending upon the habitat and extent of the drought.

During dry weather, most species of land snails of the family Achatinidae retire into their shells and secrete over the aperture an epiphragm which effectively seals the snail into its own shell. The snail does not then feed or move, and during dry weather is prevented from becoming desiccated. As soon as rain falls the epiphragm is shed and the snail becomes active. In forested areas where rainfall is frequent and there is no real seasonal drought, aestivation may last only a few days or at the most a few weeks, but in the seasonally drier savanna aestivation may last several weeks or even months. In the laboratory, achatinid snails may be kept in aestivation for three or four months (some are reported to have been kept for two or three years); they become active immediately they are put into water. Aestivation is normally confined to the dry periods, but curiously enough there are nearly always a few snails in most populations in aestivation even during the wet season. The significance of this is not known. Howes and Wells (1934), discussing water relations of slugs and snails in temperate regions, suggest that there is a tendency on the part of individuals for phases of aestivation to alternate with phases of activity even under approximately constant environmental conditions. They suggest a natural hydration cycle in the animals themselves. If this is so in the tropical African Achatinidae, some of which burrow into the ground before secreting an epiphragm, catastrophic events such as grass fires, which often destroy great numbers of snails, would spare aestivating individuals. In species that feed on crops such as the giant snail, *Achatina fulica*, most attempts at mass destruction would still leave any aestivating individuals alive, and the population could then regenerate. The giant snail can in fact aestivate for ten or twelve months, possibly longer (Mead, 1961). During this time the snails lose about sixty per cent of their body weight. Several organ systems are drawn upon for sustenance, including the reproductive system, which becomes atrophied so as to resemble superficially the juvenile condition. Aestivation in the giant snail ceases with the onset of rain. In *Limicolaria martensiana* fully formed eggs may remain viable for a month or more inside an aestivating snail. Aestivating snails can move without the stimulus of rain: direct tropical sunshine will induce *Limicolaria martensiana* to shed its epiphragm and seek shelter.

Snails of the family Achatinidae are, then, extremely sensitive to dry weather, and from hatching until breeding adults they can enter aestivation as soon as the weather becomes dry. Since snails cannot move long distances away from poor conditions, aestivation becomes of vital importance to their survival.

There are many examples of aestivation in insects, especially in species living in seasonally dry areas. Insects may aestivate in any one of the stages in their life cycle from eggs to adults, but the stage at which aestivation normally occurs is usually characteristic of the species. In the Rukwa Valley, Tanganyika, adults of the red locust, *Nomadacris septemfasciata*, emerge at the end of the rainy season in March and April. The following seven or eight months until the next rains in October and November are spent in aestivation. Norris (1962) has shown that aestivation in this species can be induced in the laboratory by artifically changing the daylength; it therefore seems possible that daylength may be a proximate stimulus in natural situations. The ultimate factor involved in the aestivation of the red locust is, however, seasonal drought.

Lunar Rhythms

A number of marine invertebrates are known to have lunar rhythms, and it has recently been shown that several species of tropical African aquatic insects also show a lunar periodicity in emergence.

In Lake Victoria adults of the mayfly, *Povilla adusta*, emerge in large numbers at the period of the full moon (Hartland-Rowe,

1955). Fig. 17 shows the days before and after full moon during which twenty-two different swarms emerged; a marked peak in emergence occurs on the second day after the full moon. Swarms of this species may be recorded simultaneously in areas as much

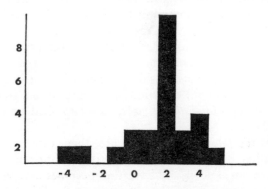

FIG. 17. Lunar periodicity in a mayfly, *Povilla adusta*, on Lake Victoria. The number of swarms is shown on the vertical axis, and days before and after full moon (o) on the horizontal axis. From Hartland-Rowe (1955).

as fifty miles apart. The adults live only a few hours, and presumably the ecological significance of such synchronised emergence is to ensure that mating is possible.

A number of other aquatic insects show a lunar periodicity in Lake Victoria, including several species of Trichoptera and Diptera (Corbet, 1958). Two species of 'lake fly', *Chaoborus*, emerge and swarm once a month at the time of the new moon. At such times great columns of flies, looking like black smoke, can be seen rising from the lake. The life cycle of these flies takes two months to complete, and hence there are two populations of each species separated in time by one month (MacDonald, 1956).

Seasonal Forms of Insects

Several morphological characters of tsetse flies, *Glossina* spp., are under climatic control, and as a result are more likely to appear at certain times of the year than at others (Glasgow, 1963). These characters include size, degree of pigmentation of the abdomen, and certain details of wing venation. Small tsetse appear when food is scarce, and also when pupae are exposed to high temperatures. High humidity produces darker flies and high temperature paler flies. Abnormalities in wing venation occur if the puparia are subject to high temperatures. Glasgow feels that these environmental variations have no survival value. This seems unlikely, but it is true that the survival value of such changes is not understood. From the practical point of view these environmentally determined characters can be used to make deductions about

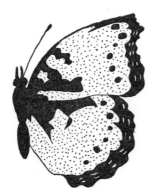

FIG. 18. The wet and dry season forms of *Precis octavia*. The wet season form (left) is mainly orange with black markings; the dry season form (right) is much darker with blue markings and very little orange. These forms are so different from each other that they could easily be mistaken for distinct species.

the sort of climate to which the flies were exposed during their earlier stages.

Several species of African butterflies have wet and dry season colour forms, evidently environmentally determined. In *Precis octavia* (Fig. 18) the wet season form is bright orange with black markings, quite different from the dry season form, which is mainly black with blue markings. In areas where wet and dry seasons alternate and where they are clearly defined, the forms replace each other seasonally. Around Kampala the dry season form is rare, but in parts of East Africa where the dry season is more pronounced it is common. An individual butterfly cannot change colour, but a dry season female can give rise to wet season offspring. In some related European butterflies it has been shown that the

AE F

stimulus to produce a particular seasonal form has to be provided during the development of the larva or pupa.

In the savanna areas of Africa the grass and other vegetation is burnt off during the dry season. This can happen naturally through dry thunderstorms during a drought and may have been going on for millions of years. Nowadays, and possibly for some thousands of years, most grass fires are started by man, for it is believed that burning the dry grass before the onset of rain improves and hastens the growth of new grass. An area of newly burnt savanna is essentially black in colour. Many species of acridid grasshoppers and other insects have black or blackish forms present among the range of colour forms normally found in unburnt habitats, and these forms are much more common on recently burnt ground. Some species may be able to change colour from green or brown to black, while in others there are black forms that may seek out an appropriate background, in this case freshly burnt grass. The occurrence of black grasshoppers on burnt ground is seasonal, and is clearly associated with burning; and in those species that have been investigated the proximate factors are bright incident light and non-reflecting background.

Daily Rhythms

During the course of a day an animal undergoes a certain rhythm in its behaviour. Such a rhythm may in some species be endogenous, but in most species external events, particularly changes in temperature, light, and the availability of food, are important. Often a population is highly synchronised in its daily behaviour: one effect of this, especially in sedentary and weak-flying species, is that the chances of mating are greatly increased.

In the savanna elephants move into the shade of trees and bushes between 10 a.m. and 5 p.m., so avoiding direct exposure to the tropical sun. Many diurnal insects do not fly until the dew has dried off the vegetation and the temperature has risen above a certain critical level. Many animals are nocturnal, and most species are active for only part of the night. Nocturnal insects are in general most active during the two or three hours after sunset and to a lesser extent just before sunrise; but there are species that have peaks of activity for other limited times during the night.

The biting cycles of Diptera have received much attention in tropical Africa because of the medical importance of some species. The East African Virus Research Institute, Entebbe, has for some time been investigating activity patterns in biting and other insects. As part of the investigations a high steel tower has been erected in a tropical forest, and insect activity at different levels has been measured quantitatively. Some of the results are published in Haddow *et al.* (1961). A photograph of the tower and the surrounding forest is shown in Plate V. Swarms of mosquitoes and tabanids have been recorded above the forest canopy at 120 feet in the Zika Forest, Uganda (Corbet and Haddow, 1962). Mosquitoes swarm at sunset while tabanids swarm at sunrise; the significance of the swarms is not known, but may well be connected with synchronised mating activity. In the Mpanga Forest, Uganda, the biting cycle of the mosquito, *Mansonia fuscopennata*, varies at different levels in the forest, and in particular the insect makes daily vertical movements (Haddow, 1961).

Diurnal and Seasonal Rhythms in an African Bird

An overall picture of rhythmic events is available for very few species of African animals. One species, a small passerine bird, the black-faced dioch, *Quelea quelea*, has been investigated in detail (Ward, 1965). This bird is extremely abundant in the drier parts of tropical Africa. It feeds chiefly on seeds of grasses, and at times does an immense amount of damage to cereal crops. In the Lake Chad region of Nigeria these birds roost together in thousands. There is a clear diurnal rhythm in their feeding activity: they leave the roost soon after dawn and fly off to the feeding grounds, where they feed for two or three hours; then they fly back and spend the hot part of the day in the roost; in the late afternoon when it becomes cooler they feed again for about two hours. Breeding takes place in the wet season, which is well-defined and predictable in this area, and at this time of the year the food consists of small seeds and immature insects. With the onset of the dry season larger seeds are eaten, and it is at this time that crops may be damaged. At the beginning of the rains many grass seeds germinate in the ground simultaneously and the food supply of the birds is suddenly diminished. The birds lay down fat, and after a time migrate to areas where the rains have been falling for some weeks and where food has become readily available again.

Thus in the black-faced dioch there is a series of adjustments to seasonal and diurnal events, in particular to the food supply. This bird is one of the few species of animals for which such information is available in tropical Africa.

Concluding Remarks

It is evident that in tropical Africa many rhythmic phenomena are stimulated by rain. Seasonal breeding is in most instances stimulated by rain, and aestivation is important in the lives of many species. Even lunar periodicity may not be unconnected with rain, as a lunar cycle of rainfall has been demonstrated statistically (Adderley and Bowen, 1962). Seasonal and other rhythms are therefore more affected by rain in the tropics than in other regions of the world.

CHAPTER 5

Ecological Genetics of Populations

Besides considering the ecology of individuals it is possible to consider the ecology of genes, in so far as the frequencies and kinds of the genes are adapted to specific environments just as are those of individuals. The study of ecological genetics involves recognition of particular genes in populations, and investigations into the significance of these genes in the lives of the organisms possessing them.

Many of the variations in structure, colour, pattern, physiology, and behaviour that occur within species of animals are genetically determined. Most genetic research is conducted in the laboratory: there have been relatively few studies of the ecological genetics of natural populations, and most of the studies that have been attempted are of organisms living in the temperate regions of Europe and North America (Ford, 1964). In Africa, ecological genetics has been considered mainly from the standpoint of medicine and agriculture. For instance, it is recognised that some people possess genes that enable them to withstand specific environmental hazards such as certain diseases; and many crops and some domestic animals have to be genetically selected in order to thrive in the tropics.

Most of the genetically determined characters observable in organisms are controlled by the combined effects of many genes: that is, they are polygenically determined. For instance, birds living in the forested regions of Africa have a darker plumage colour than birds of the same species living in the savanna regions, and such plumage colour is in general polygenically determined. There are, however, many practical difficulties in studying polygenic inheritance, and it is not surprising that ecological geneticists working in the field have concentrated their attention largely on the effects of major genes that control easily recognisable and distinct characters.

77

Polymorphism

A consideration of polymorphism has been rewarding in studies of the ecological genetics of natural populations. Polymorphism may be defined as the occurrence together of two or more distinct genetic forms of a species in such proportions that the rarest of them cannot be maintained by recurrent mutation alone. Differences due to sex, age, and season are excluded from this definition. Intermediates between the forms may occur, but by definition they must occur only at low relative frequency. Polymorphism, then, is a quantitative concept, involving the recognition of poly-modal variation within populations. Polymorphic forms within a population are normally under the control of genes having clear-cut effects in the phenotype. In general, the existence of polymorphism within a population reflects a balance of selective forces such that under certain environmental conditions one genotype is at an advantage in terms of chances of survival, while under different conditions another genotype is at an advantage. Such a balance of selective forces occurs frequently, and it is perhaps not surprising that in the complex environments of tropical Africa polymorphism is a widespread phenomenon. Genotypes giving polymorphism may be maintained in stable equilibrium within populations (1) if the fitness (capacity to survive and reproduce) of the heterozygotes is greater than that of the homozygotes, or (2) if the fitness of the genes varies with their frequency in the population, that is to say, a given gene will be at a selective advantage over another so long as it does not exceed a specified relative frequency in the population.

Sickle Cell in Man

Many examples of polymorphism maintained by heterozygote advantage are known, and one is of particular interest in tropical Africa. There is in Africa, and to a much lesser extent elsewhere, a condition of the blood in man known as sickle cell anaemia, so called because the red blood cells assume a sickle-shape *in vitro*. It is an inherited condition, and in individuals homozygous for this trait the haemoglobin within the red blood cells is slightly abnormal. In four out of five cases death from anaemia occurs before the age of reproduction. Individuals that are heterozygous for sickle cell

are normally healthy, but in addition these heterozygotes are relatively more resistant than homozygous non-sicklers to malaria
caused by *Plasmodium falciparum*. In parts of Africa where such
malaria is common, the relative frequency of sicklers is maintained
at equilibrium such that the death-rate of homozygous sicklers is
balanced by the survival-rate of the malaria-resistant heterozygotes.
In areas of intense malaria the chances of survival of a heterozygote are sixteen per cent better than those of a homozygous non-
sickler, and among some groups of East Africans the sickle cell

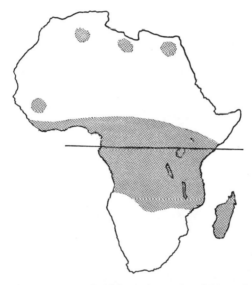

Fig. 19. The areas of Africa where the sickle cell gene is
common. From Carter (1962), after H. Lehmann.

gene reaches a frequency of forty per cent. The frequency declines towards the west and the south, and the gene does not occur
among the Bushmen. There are many irregularities in the frequency, some of which can be explained by recent population
shifts, but in general the sickle cell trait is maintained at high
relative frequency in areas of intense *falciparum* malaria. Fig. 19
shows the parts of Africa where the sickle cell trait is common.

Malaria is in part dependent upon concentrations of people, and
one would expect the percentage of sicklers to be greater in areas
of high population density. This is so in Liberia, where the sickle

cell gene reaches its highest frequencies in areas of greatest population density (Livingstone, 1962). On these grounds one might
expect both the frequency of malaria and the frequency of the
sickle cell gene to increase now that human numbers are rising so
steeply in many parts of Africa. The increasing tendency of people
to settle in specific areas rather than to move around in search of
food and other resources may also increase the chance of malaria
infection, but at the same time a more settled population would be
easier to deal with medically.

Polymorphism in Land Snails

The effect of population density on gene frequency has been
investigated in another, very different, animal in tropical Africa:
the land snail, *Limicolaria martensiana*. In Uganda this snail occurs

FIG. 20.   Colour forms of the snail, *Limicolaria martensiana*.
The snails are basically pale buff. The black areas shown
are dark brown and the shaded areas pale brown. Adult
snails are about three centimetres long. Left to right:
streaked, pallid 1, pallid 2, pallid 3.

in isolated populations, and around Kampala four distinct genetic
colour forms of the shell have been found, as shown in Fig. 20.
The three pallid forms appear to have arisen as dilute mutations
of the streaked form, since in most of the pallid shells streaking is
just discernible as pale lines. Table 10 shows the relative frequency of these four forms, and also the population density, in
ten populations around Kampala. The relative frequency of the
streaked form is greatest where the population density is low;
indeed where the snails are at a density of less than one per square
metre, almost all are streaked. The pallid forms reach high rela-

TABLE 10 Relative frequency of colour forms of *Limicolaria martensiana* in populations around Kampala, Uganda.

Popula-tion	Number examined	Per cent				Density per square metre
		streaked	pallid 1	pallid 2	pallid 3	
I	412	44·4	13·8	36·2	5·6	>100
2	616	55·0	21·0	20·0	3·9	>100
3	1,594	61·4	16·2	19·7	2·7	>100
4	3,455	68·4	15·2	12·9	3·5	26
5	1,049	75·7	10·2	12·3	1·8	21
6	512	77·8	10·7	11·5	—	8
7	411	92·6	7·4	—	—	5
8	130	97·7	2·3	—	—	<1
9	382	100·0	—	—	—	<1
10	75	100·0	—	—	—	<1

tive frequencies in populations where the population density is greater. In this species there is no evidence of heterozygous advantage, and I have suggested (Owen, 1963) that the significance of the polymorphism lies in the fact that the colour forms contrast markedly with each other. To the human eye, the streaked form appears cryptically coloured; its intricate pattern makes it difficult to see in natural situations, especially where bright sunshine and deep shade alternate. In contrast, the pallid forms do not appear cryptic, indeed they often seem conspicuous. There is evidence that a great many predators, especially birds and rodents, eat the snails. Possibly polymorphism in *Limicolaria martensiana* is maintained by what has been termed 'apostatic selection' (Clarke, 1962), in which the selective advantage of two or more contrasting colour forms lies in their conspicuous difference from each other. In theory, predators, using past experience as a guide in finding their prey, find proportionately more of a colour form with which they have already had significant success. Hence rare colour forms that contrast would be at a selective advantage because they would tend not to be recognised as prey. In addition, predators would be better able to develop a specific search-image when the population density of the prey is high than when it is low. In *Limicolaria martensiana* the streaked form may be at an advantage because of its cryptic coloration as long as the population density is not above a certain critical level, at which point contrasting non-cryptic forms assume an advantage simply because they are different. Pallid mutations occur rarely in a wide variety of otherwise cryptically coloured animals, and possibly it is only in species with locally high population densities that they are favoured by selection and come to form a significant proportion of the population.

Mimicry

Another example of the relative fitness of genes depending upon their frequency in the population is found in the polymorphic mimetic butterflies of tropical Africa. But first a consideration of what is meant by mimicry. In tropical Africa, especially in the forested regions, a great many of the larger diurnal insects, particularly butterflies, are conspicuously patterned in black and white or black and orange. Many of these insects are unpalatable to potential predators, and it has long been known that the conspicuous colour patterns function as an advertisement of their distasteful qualities. Many palatable insects mimic the colour and pattern of distasteful species to a remarkable degree, and it is assumed that they are often mistaken for unpalatable species by predators and are thus afforded protection. This does not, of course, mean that distasteful or mimetic insects are completely immune from the attacks of predators, but rather that they enjoy a slight selective advantage over palatable non-mimetic species. Two kinds of mimicry can be distinguished: Batesian mimicry, in which there is a distasteful model and a palatable mimic, and Müllerian mimicry, in which several, often unrelated, distasteful species resemble one another in colour and pattern. In practice it is often difficult to distinguish Batesian from Müllerian mimicry, and in the forests of tropical Africa there appears to be a vast assemblage of similar mimetic insects, some palatable, some distasteful. This mimetic assemblage involves many examples of polymorphism. In most cases of polymorphic mimicry, the mimics exist in a variety of sympatric colour forms, each of which matches a different distasteful species. Often it is only the females that exhibit mimetic polymorphism, the males being non-mimetic.

Among the butterflies of tropical Africa there are two important families of distasteful and unpalatable species, the Danaidae and the Acraeidae. A great many other butterflies, particularly in the families Nymphalidae, Papilionidae, Satyridae, and Lycaenidae,

FIG. 21. Models and polymorphic mimics. Right: three mimetic colour forms of *Papilio dardanus*; left: three species of models (two *Amauris* and one *Bematistes*). The heavily shaded areas are orange and the lightly shaded areas yellowish; all other areas are black or white, as shown.

are mimics of species in these two families. The most-studied mimetic butterfly is the swallowtail, *Papilio dardanus*, a member of the Papilionidae. The male of this species is pale yellow with black markings and looks like a normal swallowtail butterfly. In many (but not all) areas the females are strikingly different from the males and are highly polymorphic, each colour form bearing a strong resemblance to a species of Danaidae or Acraeidae. Some of these resemblances are shown in Fig. 21. P. M. Sheppard and C. A. Clarke have succeeded in breeding *Papilio dardanus* (in Britain) on an extensive scale, and in a series of papers (summarised in Ford, 1964) have shown that the forms are controlled by multiple alleles or by closely linked genes whose phenotypic effect is limited to the females. They find that there is complete or nearly complete dominance between sympatric forms, thus maintaining a close resemblance between mimic and model, but when forms from different parts of Africa are crossed the dominance breaks down to a large extent, and intermediate forms appear among the offspring. Hence the resemblance of mimic to model is perfected in areas where both occur and where the mimic is subject to selection. In any one area the various colour forms of *Papilio dardanus* match the available models to a remarkable degree. In addition, the relative frequency of the colour forms of the mimic is adjusted to the frequency of its available model; the mimic is normally rarer than the model, but common models have common mimics. It is clear that if mimics were too common predators would soon learn that they are palatable.

A similar situation prevails in the nymphalid butterfly, *Pseudacraea eurytus*. This is one of the most polymorphic of all butterflies, and it is common in forested regions throughout tropical Africa. Many of its colour forms are figured in colour by Carpenter (1949). Both males and females are mimetic and polymorphic, but the genetics of the polymorphism is not known. In *Pseudacraea eurytus* the occurrence and relative frequency of the mimetic forms is determined, as in *Papilio dardanus*, by the occurrence and relative frequency of the model species, in this case butterflies of the acraeid genus, *Bematistes*.

Polymorphism in mimetic assemblages of butterflies is usually confined to the species that mimic, but there are a few polymorphic models. An example is *Danaus chrysippus*, an undoubtedly distasteful species that occurs in four distinct colour forms. These

FIG. 22. Müllerian mimicry. Right: four colour forms of *Danaus chrysippus*; from top to bottom, *chrysippus*, *alcippus*, *dorippus*, *albinus*. Left: four colour forms of *Acraea encedon*; from top to bottom, *encedon*, *alcippina*, *daira*, *alcippina-daira*. The shaded areas are orange; the remaining areas are black or white, as shown.

forms are shown in Fig. 22. The relative frequency of the forms varies in different parts of Africa: *alcippus* is the only form in many parts of the West, while in the drier areas of Kenya *dorippus* is most frequent. All four forms occur around Kampala: *chrysippus* is the most frequent, followed in turn by *alcippus*, *dorippus*, and *albinus*. Each of the four forms of *Danaus chrysippus* is matched by a form of yet another distasteful polymorphic species, *Acraea encedon*. The forms of *Acraea encedon* are shown side by side with those of *Danaus chrysippus* in Fig. 22. Around Kampala, the *encedon* form is the most frequent, followed in turn by *alcippina*, *daira*, and *alcippina-daira*. The chances of the corresponding forms of these two species being similarly ranked is only one in twenty-four; not only do the four forms in each species match each other in colour and pattern, but the frequencies of each are similarly ranked. It is clear that since both *Danaus chrysippus* and *Acraea encedon* are distasteful species they fit the definition of Müllerian mimics. But why they should be similarly polymorphic is obscure. Possibly there are opposing selective forces, one producing similarity through Müllerian mimicry, the other producing contrast and diversity through the operation of apostatic selection (page 81). The genetics of mimetic polymorphism in *Danaus chrysippus* and *Acraea encedon* has not been fully investigated. I have evidence that in *Acraea encedon* multiple alleles are involved, and that the common *encedon* form is recessive to most other forms. Both species are butterflies of open country and forest edge, and occur together, but since both are also models for other Müllerian and Batesian mimics the situation is likely to prove extremely complex. *Acraea encedon* has a number of other polymorphic forms which do not resemble any forms of *Danaus chrysippus*.

Polymorphism and Background Colour

Polymorphic mimicry, then, involves both a qualitative and a quantitative adjustment between two or more species. Similar adjustments may occur between polymorphic species and the colours of the background against which they live.

In many parts of the world, and especially in the tropics, there are two main background colours against which animals may conceal themselves, one green, the other brown. Many small terrestrial animals are green or brown, and many instances of green-brown polymorphism are known, especially in the larvae and pupae of butterflies and in the nymphs and adults of grasshoppers. In East Africa a grasshopper, *Homorocoryphus nitidulus*, occurs in six distinct colour forms: green, brown, green with purple stripes, brown with purple stripes, green with a purple head, and brown with a purple head. Although there is some variation in colour within each form, all are distinct from each other. Table 11 shows

TABLE 11 Relative frequency of colour forms of *Homorocoryphus nitidulus* at Kampala, Uganda.

Colour form	Number examined	Per cent
green	6,682	63·34
brown	3,521	33·38
green with purple stripes	305	2·89
green with purple head	34	0·32
brown with purple head	5	0·05
brown with purple stripes	2	0·02

the relative frequency of the six forms in a random sample of about ten thousand specimens collected at Kampala, Uganda. Green is about twice as frequent as brown, and together these two forms comprise nearly ninety-seven per cent of the sample. The remaining four forms are relatively rare, together comprising 3·28 per cent. The colour forms occur in both sexes, but there is a statistical association of green with females and brown with males. *Homorocoryphus nitidulus* lives in grass in somewhat damp and humid places. The green form matches living grass exactly; likewise the brown matches dead grass. The purple on the remaining four forms bears a striking resemblance to the purple areas of anthocyanin pigment that occur on grass leaves and stems in the habitats in which the grasshoppers live. There seems little doubt that in the habitats of *Homorocoryphus nitidulus* green is the predominant colour, brown is easily next, and the purple on green and brown leaves and stems is the rarest. Hence the three conspicuous colours in the habitat of the grasshopper are the same colours that occur in the grasshoppers themselves; these colours can be similarly ranked in both the habitat and the grasshopper, suggesting that each of the forms is adapted not only to the colour but also to the amount of that colour in the background.

The ability to change colour may in some animals be super-imposed upon polymorphic variation. In the side-striped chame-leon, *Chameleo bitaeniatus*, the young are basically brown, and their ability to undergo reversible colour change is limited to different shades of brown: they cannot change to a very different colour. Adult males are basically turquoise-blue with a dark reddish-purple dorsal crest, a yellowish gular crest, and a mid-lateral line that lacks pigment, bordered ventrally by a broken reddish purple line. Adult females lack the conspicuous crest pat-terns and are basically either green or brown. Reversible colour change occurs in the adults of both sexes: they become darker at lower and paler at higher temperatures, darker in bright daylight and paler at night, and the entire colour and pattern is intensified (especially in the males) upon meeting another chameleon or when attacked by a predator. The males, then, are alike, while the females are either green or brown. Around Kampala, Uganda, green females are about three times as frequent as brown (Ogilvie and Owen, 1964). There is no evidence that adult females can change from green to brown or from brown to green. Hence in this chameleon the females occur in two distinct colour forms and in addition possess an ability to change the intensity of their basic colour under different environmental stimuli. This results in con-siderable diversity in colour and pattern within a population at any one time, especially if, as is often the case, there are differences of light and temperature in different parts of the habitat. Such diversity may afford a considerable degree of protection from pre-dators liable to form visual search images, such as snakes and birds. It may be noted that the restriction of the basic polymorphism to the females is paralleled by some polymorphic mimetic butterflies, including *Papilio dardanus*.

The ability to change colour superimposed upon a basic poly-morphism may occur in other tropical African animals, particularly cichlid fish. The difficulty in most cases is to separate by experi-ment genetic and environmental colours. It is clear, however, that the combination of environmentally induced colour changes and genetic polymorphisms imparts a good deal of variation in colour and pattern to individuals within a population. The resulting diversity may be especially advantageous at high population densities and where predators are abundant: some of the most polymorphic and variable animals are extremely common species.

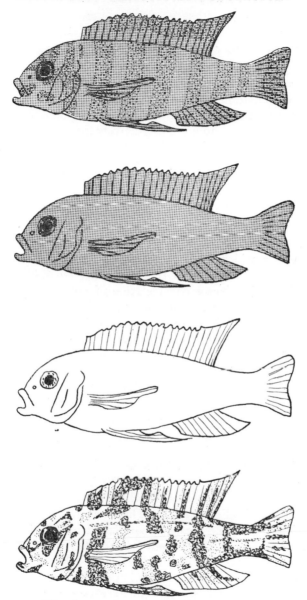

FIG. 23.   The four colour forms of *Pseudotropheus zebra*.
The shaded bands in the upper specimen are bluish; the
lower specimen is intricately mottled with dark and light
brown. From Fryer (1959).

Speciation

Speciation, or the formation of new species, is thought to occur when populations become geographically isolated from one another; once isolated, populations can respond through selection to different environments, and can, in time, become genetically different from the original stock. If such populations eventually meet they may prove to be reproductively incompatible; that is to say, they are by definition different species. Undoubtedly this process has occurred repeatedly among the animals of tropical Africa, and has given rise to the enormous number of species. But direct evidence of its occurrence is lacking; no one has ever demonstrated speciation through geographical isolation, chiefly because most species probably take thousands of generations to evolve.

There is a widespread feeling that all species evolve by the process outlined above. But there are other possibilities, at least one of which involves a consideration of polymorphism. It has been found that in some animals there is non-random mating between polymorphic colour forms. This may be assortative (preferential mating of like forms) or disassortative (preferential mating of unlike forms). Assortative mating increases the genetic variance of a population because fewer intermediates (heterozygotes) are produced. Nearly complete assortative mating of genetic forms within a population could, given time, provide the necessary isolation between members of a population for speciation to begin. Is there evidence of assortative mating among tropical African animals?

The East African lakes are famous for the number of sympatric species of cichlid fish; each of the major lakes has many endemic species: there are 180 species of cichlid in Lake Nyasa, and all but four are endemic (Fryer, 1959). There has in the past been much discussion of possible means of speciation in the cichlids in the East African lakes. The current view is that speciation has occurred through geographical isolation and selection, and that in general the mechanism of speciation in these fish has been no different from what is thought to have occurred in most other animals. Kosswig (1947) postulated that assortative mating may have been important in speciation among the East African cichlids, but his view has been repeatedly challenged by other workers in the field. At this point it may be noted that some of the cichlids are very polymorphic in colour and in pattern. For instance, *Pseudotropheus zebra* occurs in a variety of distinct forms, four of which are shown in Fig. 23. Several observers have noted that like forms tend to stay in shoals. No one has ever demonstrated that wild cichlid fish undergo assortative mating, but on the other hand no one has ever shown that they mate at random. Here is an important unsolved problem in ecological genetics; a problem that could contribute to theories of speciation and to understanding why there are so many different species of cichlids in the East African Lakes.

The Effects of Isolation

The importance of isolation in the formation of new species has just been considered. There is no doubt that ecological and geographical isolation has fundamental effects upon the likelihood of occurrence and the frequency of particular genes in animal populations. Even quite small distances can evidently act as major barriers to the dispersal of genes from one population to another. A great many animals, although presumably physically capable of moving from one population to another, in fact do not. Hence some populations geographically close together may be genetically quite different. Two examples, both from insects, may be considered.

TABLE 12 Relative frequency (per cent) of colour forms in populations of the butterfly, *Acraea encedon*, around Kampala, Uganda.

Colour form	Population				
	Entebbe	Kazi	Kololo	Makerere	Kawanda
encedon	46·0	49·9	62·4	62·2	67·3
alcippina	—	1·1	28·4	26·7	18·5
daira	15·9	15·2	3·9	5·6	8·4
lycia	30·2	25·2	1·0	0·4	1·2
others, including alcippina-daira	7·9	8·6	4·3	5·1	4·6
Total examined	63	473	306	288	407

Note: *encedon*, *alcippina*, *daira*, and *alcippina-daira* are illustrated in Fig. 22. Form *lycia* has the same pattern as *encedon*, but the orange is replaced by white.

The butterfly, *Acraea encedon*, has already been discussed under mimicry. It will be recalled that the species is polymorphic in colour and pattern. Around Kampala it occurs in a variety of colour forms, four of the mimetic forms being shown in Fig. 22. There are in addition several other colour forms, including one in which the orange is replaced by white; this form is called *lycia*. *Acraea encedon* is not a strong-flying species and many populations are to a large extent isolated from each other. Table 12 shows the relative frequency of the colour forms in five populations around Kampala. All the populations are close together, some are less than a mile apart, and the greatest distance, between Kawanda and Entebbe, is twenty miles. As shown in Table 12, *encedon* is the commonest form in all populations, but its frequency varies from 46·0 to 67·3 per cent. Form *alcippina* is frequent at Kololo, Makerere, and Kawanda, but is rare at Kazi, and absent from Entebbe. Form *lycia* reaches 30·2 per cent at Entebbe and 25·2 per cent at Kazi, but elsewhere it is rare. There are, then, striking differences in the relative frequency of the genetically determined

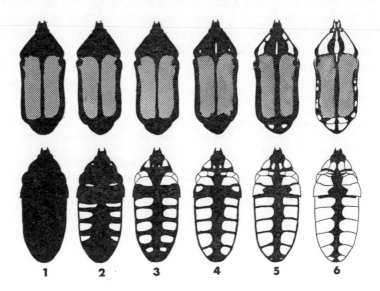

FIG. 24. The six colour forms of the beetle, *Gnathocera trivittata*. These six forms are a graded series from 1, the darkest, to 6, the palest. The shaded areas are orange, the white areas pale yellow, and the black areas dark brown.

colour forms in this species in different populations. These differences could only be maintained if there is complete or almost complete lack of interchange of individuals between the populations.

The second insect illustrating the effects of isolation is a beetle. *Gnathocera trivittata* occurs throughout tropical Africa from coast to coast. The adults feed on the pollen of many species of grass, and during bright sunshine they may be found sitting on the flower heads of grass. They are about eighteen millimetres long, and where they occur they are conspicuous. In Uganda they are confined to grassy savanna, and are especially associated with hillsides and hill tops. In colour they are strikingly orange and black, with or without yellow markings on the upper- and underside. These yellow markings vary between individuals. Six forms can be recognised, forming a graded series from 1, in which the yellow markings are absent, to 6, in which they are conspicuous. The forms are shown in Fig. 24. Forms 2 to 5 can be regarded as intermediates between 1 and 6. Table 13 shows the relative frequency of the forms in five populations in Uganda. At Kololo and Naguru intermediates are frequent, while at Kazi, Paraa and Lake Kitagata intermediates are rare or absent. Kololo and Naguru are adjacent hills separated by half a mile of habitat that is unsuitable for beetles. Each of these hills has a mode at 1, but the 19·5 per cent difference in the relative frequency of 1 is statistically significant. Hence the two populations are similar in that they both tend towards bimodality in variation, but they differ in the frequency of the forms. Kazi is about ten miles from Kololo, and Paraa is about 175 miles from Kazi. Yet Kazi is very different from Kololo in that there is a conspicuous single mode at 5 and 6, while at the same time it is very similar to Paraa, despite the large

TABLE 13 Relative frequency (per cent) of colour forms in populations of the beetle, *Gnathocera trivittata*, in Uganda.

Population	Colour form						Number examined
	1	2	3	4	5	6	
Kololo	72·0	4·3	5·5	0·6	11·2	6·4	328
Naguru	52·5	2·0	2·0	5·1	12·1	26·3	99
Kazi	—	—	1·0	—	16·5	82·5	204
Paraa	—	—	—	—	2·9	97·1	35
Lake Kitagata	62·5	—	—	—	—	37·5	251

distance between these populations. Lake Kitagata, about 190 miles west of Kololo, Naguru, and Kazi, is quite different from any of the other populations: there are two modes, one at 1 and the other at 6, but there are no intermediates.

Both *Acraea encedon* and *Gnathocera trivittata* illustrate the effects of isolation upon the genetic structure of populations; other examples could be given, and many others await investigation.

Ecological Genetics, Ecology, and Taxonomy

An ecologist relies heavily upon good taxonomic work on the group of animals in which he is interested. The study of ecological genetics, and in particular of polymorphism, has had and is continuing to have important consequences with regard to the existing knowledge of species. It is now realised that many species are much more variable than was previously thought, and that many other 'species' are in fact polymorphic forms of a single species.

FIG. 25. The two female forms of *Papilio phorcas*. The shaded areas are bright emerald-green, the white areas pale yellow, and the black areas black. Males are all like the green and black female.

Thus in the land snail genus, *Limicolaria*, about 170 species have been described for Africa, mostly based upon differences in the colour and pattern of the shell. It is now known that the snails in this genus are highly variable and polymorphic, and it is likely that once populations have been thoroughly investigated it will be found that there may be no more than a dozen species in tropical Africa. Similarly in the polymorphic *Chlorophoneus* shrikes (common birds in tropical Africa), there are a variety of strikingly different colour forms, and there has until recently been a tendency to consider some of these forms as distinct species, simply because they look so different. The butterflies shown in Fig. 25 illustrate the point extremely well. They are females of *Papilio phorcas*, a common species in many parts of tropical Africa. These strikingly different colour forms are found in the same areas. They are controlled by a single gene difference, evidently sex-limited in effect. The significance of such female-limited polymorphism is obscure: mimicry does not appear to be involved. Any butterfly collector could be forgiven for mistaking them as different species.

Differences between individuals in a population have long been neglected by population ecologists. At the same time, taxonomists have frequently been confused by the genetic variation found within populations. The fact that individuals vary qualitatively may be of fundamental importance in determining population sizes and densities. The study of polymorphism in natural populations has emphasised this point. In tropical Africa, where a great many animals are variable and polymorphic, investigations into the ecological genetics of species should prove most illuminating.

CHAPTER 6

The Ecology of Man
in Tropical Africa

Whatever special qualities man may attribute to man, there is no doubt that from the standpoint of ecology man is an animal with animal needs. Man is also an abundant animal. And unlike most species, man is increasing in numbers very rapidly. This increase is relatively recent, and in tropical Africa has occurred chiefly in the past fifty or a hundred years. The present situation is that some African countries may double their population in the next twenty or thirty years. An abundant large animal always presents problems of particular ecological interest because such an animal is likely to have far-reaching effects on many other species.

Human Numbers in Tropical Africa

It is hard to say how many people there are in tropical Africa. Much of the area is not densely populated by European standards, and the population density is nothing like that of India, China, or Japan. But people seem to occur in almost all habitats, except in the drier savanna and high on mountains. Most people live in what could be described as rural areas; this is in contrast to Europe, where most people live in towns and cities.

Several recent censuses in Nigeria have given widely different human population counts. There are evidently difficulties in counting people in Africa. In 1959 there were just over six and a half million people in Uganda, an increase of 31·8 per cent over the 1948 figure. This represents a cumulative annual increase of two and a half per cent. The population of Uganda in 1980 could exceed twelve million and by the year 2000 could be twenty-five million. How many people can Uganda support? No one knows.

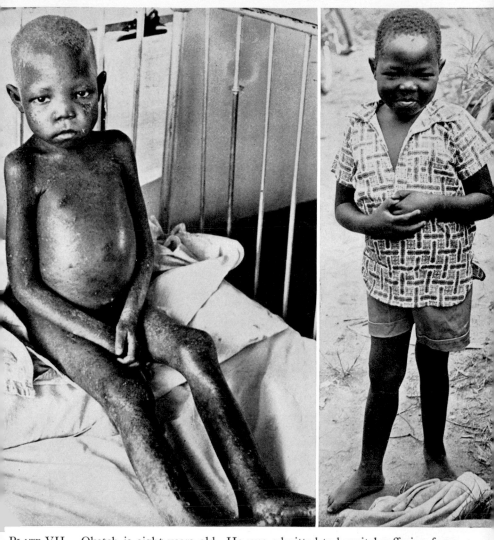

PLATE VII. Oketch is eight years old. He was admitted to hospital suffering from severe protein deficiency. His tribe are traditionally millet-eaters, but at his home they have changed to the more readily available bananas and cassava. As can be seen in the left-hand picture, his face was swollen, his skin was in bad condition, and his limb muscles were underdeveloped; at this time he was incapable of normal activities. In hospital he was treated with milk for three weeks, and when strong enough to walk was sent home. A week later he was found lying on the ground at his home; all the dried milk given him was stacked in a corner of the house and was unused. He was taken back to hospital and kept for eight weeks. Now, as can be seen in the right-hand picture, he is well and goes to school. Protein deficiency can often be cured by an adequate supply of milk, as in this case, but it could easily be prevented by eating beans, meat and fish instead of nothing but bananas and cassava. (Photographs by Erasmus Harland.)

PLATE VIII. A market scene in tropical Africa. Green cooking bananas, sweet potatoes, and cassava are stacked everywhere. There is cheap food for all, but the food contains little protein. A diet of banana and cassava is the cause of the condition of the boy shown in Plate VII. (Photograph by Ministry of Information, Uganda.)

PLATE IX.   This little boy is holding a handful of edible grasshoppers, *Homorocoryphus nitidulus*.   In many parts of tropical Africa this species occurs in immense swarms at certain times of the year. This boy would not suffer from protein deficiency if he ate plenty of grasshoppers, but unfortunately the insects are seasonal and are not available all the year round. (Photograph by C. F. H. Rowell.)

PLATE X. Collecting tsetse flies, *Glossina* spp., from a cow for laboratory research. Tsetse flies transmit trypanosomiasis, a disease of man, cattle, and wild mammals. Much money and effort have been spent on attempts to destroy tsetse flies, but the disease persists in many parts of tropical Africa. (Photograph by British Information Service, Uganda. (British Crown Copyright.)

PLATE XI.   A coffee plantation in felled tropical forest in southern Uganda.   Some trees are left for shade.   Grass has spread in between the coffee trees, and many insects that are associated with grass have colonised such plantations.   The fauna of coffee plantations has been very little investigated, apart from the insect pests of coffee trees.   (Photograph by C. H. F. Rowell.)

PLATE XII.   The impact of man on the hills of Kigezi, western Uganda.   The pale flowers are pyrethrum, which is grown commercially for the manufacture of insecticides.   On the right is a plantation of introduced Australian gums, *Eucalyptus* sp.   Terraced cultivation may be seen on the hillside in the middle distance.   These hills are wet and cool and support a flourishing agriculture and a high human population density.   At one time the mountain gorilla occurred on these hills, and it is still found in similar but uninhabited areas.   (Photograph by the Ministry

PLATE XIII. A remarkable human activity in tropical Africa. The picture shows a white rhinoceros, *Ceratotherium simum*, being captured alive and transported from Madi, Uganda for release in the Murchison Falls National Park. It is felt that white rhinoceroses are in danger of being exterminated by poachers in Madi, and that they should therefore be moved to a national park. It is presumed that ecological conditions in the Murchison Falls Park (where they do not occur naturally) are suitable for them, but whether this is so remains to be seen. (Photograph by John Blower.)

And no one knows how many people any other tropical African country can support. All that can be said is that large areas of tropical Africa appear to be under-populated by comparison with many other parts of the world. The potentialities for agricultural and industrial development in tropical Africa are largely unknown. The problem is a complex and bewildering one. An animal ecologist can only state the general nature of the problem and compare man with other animals.

Food and Nutrition

Most species of animals are comparatively restricted in diet and the kind of food eaten by a species throughout its geographical range does not vary enormously. The diet of man, however, varies conspicuously in different parts of the range. In some areas man is an almost complete herbivore, while in others he is a carnivore. In many parts of Africa human populations are completely dependent upon one or two crops: banana and cassava are two such crops. In other parts of Africa man is a carnivore: some groups of people depend entirely upon their cattle.

In tropical Africa as a whole people are dependent upon crops that they grow for themselves. These crops, which include banana, sweet potato, cassava, maize, paw-paw, and beans, were all introduced from other parts of the world, chiefly from tropical America and tropical Asia. It is remarkable that the vast equatorial forest of Africa has not produced a single important plant that can be cultivated for human food. There are of course many edible fruits in the forest, but these are only suitable for gathering, and have not thus far been cultivated.

There is no overall shortage of food in most parts of tropical Africa, although, as will be discussed later, in areas subject to seasonal drought there may be temporary shortage of food. Many of the staple crops grow easily with a minimum of attention, and in many areas they are non-seasonal. Freshwater fish are abundant in most of the larger lakes, and in some areas have hardly been exploited. Edible insects, such as termites and grasshoppers, are available in considerable quantity at certain times of the year. Large land snails are common in many areas, but are not eaten to any extent east of the Congo. Cattle and goats flourish in some areas, but cannot be kept in other regions because of disease, especially trypanosomiasis. Edible wild mammals and birds are available, but nowadays are not eaten to any great extent: the lack of interest in small birds as human food is striking in comparison with the Mediterranean countries. Most of the people living in tropical Africa depend upon locally grown food, and a very large number do not buy food but grow their own.

But although there is at present no food shortage in tropical Africa, there is in many areas a shortage of protein. This shortage is mostly due to what is loosely called 'tradition'. That is to say, people eat crops that are protein-deficient even though it would be perfectly possible to grow other crops rich in protein. Thus protein deficiency is decided more by the community's tradition of food preference than by the agricultural potentialities of the area; some of the poorest agricultural areas have little or no protein deficiency. Cooking bananas and cassava, which are staples in many parts of tropical Africa, consist almost entirely of carbohydrates with only a fraction of protein, yet many people exist on little else. In southern Uganda, ninety per cent of the children show signs of protein deficiency at some stage. The effects of protein deficiency are especially obvious in children who have just been weaned from the breast and have been changed to a diet of carbohydrate: children one to three years old are highly susceptible. In extreme cases the skin and hair are deficient in melanin pigment and there may be a retardation in mental development, which of course is likely to have serious consequences later on. Few children actually die of protein deficiency, but many suffer from it. It probably does not affect the later reproductive capacity of adults, and because poor-quality food is readily available the numbers of people increase.

In southern Uganda the main meal of the day consists of a large quantity of steamed cooking banana or other carbohydrate staple. Sauces made from groundnuts, mushrooms, certain kinds of green leaves, cherry tomatoes, and beans are eaten with the steamed bananas. Then there may be side dishes of eggs, meat (preferably tough), fish, and (when in season) termites and grasshoppers. Such a meal may take up to five hours to prepare; descriptions of the methods used and recipes for sauces are given by Rutishauser (1962). A meal such as this is extremely filling, but often only very small quantities of sauces and side dishes are available, and hence the average meal is deficient in protein. Edible grasshoppers occur in great numbers at certain times of the year and then people that eat them probably receive more protein than usual. The protein intake could be easily increased by eating more beans, which grow well in southern Uganda, and efforts are being made to encourage this. But steamed bananas are much loved and are readily available, and traditions die hard.

In Gambia (unlike Uganda) there is considerable seasonal change in the availability of the staple crops. Cereals such as findi, maize, rice, bulrush, millet, and sorghum succeed each other through the year. The diet is predominantly carbohydrate and is supplemented by small amounts of meat, fish, groundnuts, beans, and various seasonal leaves and fruits. At certain times of the year the Gambian cultivators have little or no work, while at other times they expend a great deal of energy in preparing the ground for cultivation. When the heavy work starts energy expenditure exceeds intake and body tissue is drawn upon. There is thus a seasonal change in body weight associated with fluctuations in the food supply and the amount of energy expended in preparing the ground for cultivation (Harrison *et al.*, 1964).

Poor nutrition of the mother affects the birth weight of babies. Table 14 shows the mean birth weights of babies born in hospitals in Accra, Ghana, to poor Africans, wealthy Africans, and Europeans. The mean weight of wealthy Africans and Europeans is very similar and is considerably higher than that of poor Africans. Wealthy Africans have an essentially European diet, and the low birth weight of poor Africans is partly the effect of poor nutrition. Many babies born to poor Africans are premature and hence are

TABLE 14 Mean birth weights (single births) of babies born at Accra, Ghana. From Hollingsworth (1960).

| | *Weight in pounds* | | |
	poor Africans	*wealthy Africans*	*Europeans*
males	6·62 (475)	7·07 (105)	7·34 (328)
females	6·09 (442)	6·97 (96)	6·97 (285)

Note: Figures in brackets are the numbers of babies weighed.

small; the high rate of prematurity is apparently caused by malaria. About a quarter of the babies of poor Africans born in a hospital in Ghana were premature and particularly small

(Hollingsworth, 1960). In South Africa, where malaria is less frequent, only half as many babies are born prematurely. There would appear little doubt that the combined effects of poor nutrition for the mother, malaria and, later on, deficiency in protein for the baby, result in a poor start for the child.

Disease

It is not my intention in this book to review the extensive literature on the ecology of human disease in tropical Africa. It can be said, however, that tropical Africa is one of the most disease-ridden areas of the world, and that a great many people die every year from diseases that are rare or absent in other parts of the world. And besides the diseases that are especially associated with Africa, there are others that have been imported from outside.

It is possible that until recently human numbers in tropical Africa were limited by disease. In general disease is transmitted more rapidly and its effects are more conspicuous at high than at low population densities; as a result any tendency on the part of a population to increase rapidly is likely to be checked by disease. Many of the diseases that once caused enormous mortality in human populations can now be controlled by the use of drugs and vaccines. Malaria is one such disease; indeed it is likely that malaria was until recently directly or indirectly responsible for the death of most people in tropical Africa. Much of the mortality from malaria occurs early in life, usually before the individual has reproduced. The rapid rise in human numbers in Africa in recent years may be largely because malaria no longer kills so many people in childhood.

But although drugs and vaccines can have conspicuous success with certain diseases, there are others where even now there is insufficient knowledge to control the disease successfully. Trypanosomiasis is one such disease. This disease is transmitted to man and other mammals (including cattle) by tsetse flies, *Glossina* spp. There is at present no effective vaccine against trypanosomiasis, and attempts to eradicate it have mostly been directed at destroying the tsetse flies and their habitat. In some areas drugs are being used to combat human trypanosomiasis.

Bilharzia is another disease that is widespread and abundant in tropical Africa. It is caused by two species of schistosomes,

Schistosoma mansoni and *Schistosoma haematobium*; the inter-mediate hosts are aquatic snails. *Schistosoma mansoni* causes intestinal bilharzia, and occurs in the wetter parts of tropical Africa; in some areas all the people are infected. It does not often kill, but seems to account for a great deal of general lethargy. *Schistosoma haematobium* causes urinary bilharzia, and occurs throughout Africa from Egypt to Madagascar and is especially associated with drier areas. It is less common in equatorial Africa, but in parts of Egypt it is said that red urine is regarded as normal, so prevalent is the disease. Bilharzia can be cured, but the present drugs are too toxic for widespread use, and most people that are infected do not show obvious symptoms. Attempts are being made to destroy the snails that carry the schistosomes.

Many insects contribute to man's discomfort, not so much by transmitting disease, but by causing irritation and sucking blood. Thus, staphylinid beetles of the genus *Paederus* contain in their haemolymph a vesicating toxin causing severe vesicular dermatitis and irritation when applied to the eyes and skin of man: clinical complications may follow. From time to time there are wide-spread outbreaks of these beetles (which are attracted to artificial light, and so to man) and many people are affected (McCrae and Visser, 1963). The Congo floor maggot, *Auchmeromyia luteola*, is the larva of a fly which is an intermittent ectoparasite of man. The adult flies feed upon human faeces and the larvae live on the floors of houses among matting and bedding. From time to time they attach themselves to a sleeping man and suck blood (Garrett-Jones, 1951). They probably do little harm, but with other irritant animals and diseases contribute to the general discomfort of man in tropical Africa.

New tropical African diseases are still being discovered. Early in 1959 a major epidemic virus disease, somewhat resembling dengue, broke out in north-western Uganda and rapidly spread south-eastwards across the country. The disease originated in the Congo and probably spread into the Sudan. About 750,000 cases were reported in East Africa, but no one died as a result of the disease. The disease became known as O'nyong-nyong. It causes bad headache, joint and back pains, and an itching rash (Haddow *et al.*, 1960). It is likely that such an epidemic could have con-spicuous effects on people already suffering from bilharzia, malaria, and protein deficiency.

To summarise: it would seem that disease must have played an important part in limiting human numbers in tropical Africa. Malnutrition may also have contributed but was probably not directly responsible for limiting population growth. Numbers of people are now rising steeply, largely because of improved medical knowledge and facilities; there is also an increased tendency to understand the nutritional value of food.

The Impact of Man on Other Animals and Plants

The most conspicuous effect of man on other animals and plants is that he destroys habitats to suit his own expanding needs. Much of the equatorial forest region shown in Fig. 2 has now been felled either for timber or in order to grow crops. Some forest has since regenerated, but the area of original untouched forest is now quite small. Such widespread alteration of a stable environment must have important effects on the animals living therein. Except in a few cases, these effects are virtually uninvestigated.

The savanna is grazed by cattle and in many areas cattle have replaced the indigenous ungulates. Swamps have been drained and irrigation projects are developing. There has been much erosion as the result of over-grazing and the felling of trees, and there is a danger of reduction in soil fertility as the result of these activities. Felled forest and forest-edge provide excellent ground for the cultivation of staples such as bananas, cassava, and sweet potatoes, and also for coffee which is in many areas the most important cash crop. Coffee is an extremely easy crop to grow in cleared forest, and many tropical African countries are in danger of over-producing it.

An area of forest cleared of many of its trees and planted with coffee is by no means impoverished as far as wild animals are concerned. Many insects and birds move into clearings created by this kind of agriculture, and there is a rich, but different, fauna. Grass spreads into the areas between coffee trees, and grassland animals follow. Acridid grasshoppers are rare or absent in closed tropical forest, but they are common where man has made clearings which grass and forbs have colonised.

In many parts of tropical Africa plantations of Australian gums, *Eucalyptus* spp., have been grown. These trees grow quickly and yield good timber; they also facilitate drainage. The ground flora of some of these gum plantations also consists mainly of introduced plants, such as *Lantana camara* and *Bryophyllum pinnatum*. The plantation floor is sometimes rich in native animals, particularly insects, millipedes, and land molluscs; presumably these have all recently become adapted to the different environment provided by the gum plantations. The gum trees themselves are poor in animals, and there are relatively few species of breeding birds, but the trees are used as roosts by birds and fruit bats.

Some of the introduced crops of tropical Africa have insect pests that lower the yield. Some of these pests are introduced, but many native species have moved on to a new (but often related) diet. Insecticides and methods of biological control are being developed to limit the numbers of pests of cotton and coffee, and to a lesser extent those of the staple food crops. Many of the staple crops, however, do not at present have pests that significantly affect food production. Many insects feed on banana plants, but none has yet become a major pest. The situation may change if large areas are cultivated with single crops; at present the agriculture is on a small scale with considerable diversity and with gaps of uncultivated country. Tropical Africa seems to have been more resistant than some parts of the world to introduced pests. In Uganda, there are few common animals that are not native species, in marked contrast to, say, North America and New Zealand. Some of the common plants are introduced species, and a few, such as *Lantana camara* from tropical America, are likely to become agricultural weeds.

Some tropical African animals have become pests in other parts of the world but not in Africa. The giant snail, *Achatina fulica*, is confined to the coastal belt of East Africa. It has been introduced by man, both deliberately and accidentally, to many other tropical areas from India to Hawaii, and does an enormous amount of damage to crops. There is no evidence of it having spread in Africa, despite intensive cultivation in regions bordering its natural distribution.

The creation of national parks in East and Central Africa primarily for the preservation of the large numbers of ungulates and their associated predators has brought special problems, some of them unexpected. Under protection large herbivorous mammals tend to increase in numbers, and in some cases have seriously over-grazed their own habitat; elephants have contributed to the destruction and retreat of the forest in some areas. The hippopotamus is in places so abundant as to cause erosion and destruction of grassland, and cropping programmes have been started to restore the numbers to equilibrium.

Large predatory mammals have in places been nearly or completely exterminated. It is said that the destruction of leopards by man has resulted in a rise in the baboon population, but no one knows if this is really so. Some large mammals will quickly take advantage of crops grown by man. In parts of the Congo, the chimpanzee feeds largely on the fruits of cultivated paw-paws, some monkeys are destructive in banana gardens, and baboons are destructive in millet fields.

There are in Africa several species of freshwater fish that can be fished and marketed on a large scale. The problem of over-fishing is not yet a serious one in most areas, but there will come a time when the availability of fish will decline. Some tropical lakes appear to be rich and can produce greater weights of fish per acre than any comparable freshwater areas in the world, but their productivity is nothing like that of temperate marine environments.

One of the most controversial effects of man's activities in the drier parts of tropical Africa is the periodic burning of grassland. Throughout the savanna, grass is burnt off whenever the weather is dry. It is assumed that burning results in better grass for cattle and for wild ungulates. There may, however, be other effects, particularly in the nitrate cycle in the soil, and the smoke pall from an extensive grass fire can induce rainfall. It is possible that since large-scale burning began there has been an increase in the area occupied by grassy savanna at the expense of forest. In parts of East Africa the air for hundreds of square miles may be filled with smoke from grass fires; the effect of this on human health is not known. One ecological result of grass fires is that animals that cannot move quickly are destroyed in great numbers. Many birds, such as swallows, kites, and bee-eaters, will gather around the edge of a fire and feed on winged insects trying to escape.

Lastly, there are some unexpected effects that man may have upon animals. In Sierra Leone chimpanzees have become scavengers of refuse left by man, and feed upon man's crops. One effect is that longevity of the chimpanzee is increased; another is that there is increased dental decay among them resulting from infection from human refuse (Jones and Cave, 1960). In East

Chad it is said that people scavenge food from lion kills, as indeed they do in Uganda. But in East Chad people put out water for the lions during the dry season.

Prospects

Evidently human numbers in Africa will continue to rise steeply. Human needs will also increase. It is obvious, if one is to predict future changes in the suitability of tropical Africa for high human population densities, that there will be an increased need for sound ecological information about many of the species that in one way or another influence or are influenced by man. Long-term ecological studies of animals of direct importance to man have been undertaken, but there is much scope for detailed studies, not only of species that are directly important to man but of all species and communities. It is to be hoped that the research organisations and universities of tropical Africa will continue to initiate and expand such studies: information is badly needed.

AE H

CHAPTER 7

Ecological Research
in Tropical Africa

It is apparent from what has been said in this book that in tropical
Africa there are many ecological problems that are uninvestigated
or that await detailed, and in particular quantitative, analysis.
Many of the countries comprising tropical Africa are not wealthy
and there are only limited financial resources available for zoological research. Indeed it would be inappropriate for the universities
and other research organisations of tropical Africa to spend large
sums of money on the expensive equipment that is needed for
basic research in many fields of zoology today.

Zoological research in tropical Africa should have a strong
ecological flavour. There are few places in the world that are as
suitable or as interesting for ecological research as the African
tropics. In addition, most of the countries of tropical Africa are
agricultural, and many agricultural problems are fundamentally
ecological. Research in animal ecology certainly need not be expensive: most of the topics discussed in this book need little more
than a pencil and paper for investigation. Picking the right animals
in order to solve particular problems is often difficult, and it is
important for the individual research worker to be opportunist
and to take advantage of readily available local species. Thus,
although attractive to the newcomer to Africa, research on the
large mammals of the savanna is likely to prove expensive: similar
problems can be tackled more effectively in smaller animals. The
individual research worker and school or university student would
be best to concentrate on small animals, such as insects which are
everywhere abundant and readily available.

One problem that is immediately encountered by the potential
animal ecologist in Africa is that of identification of species.

Frequently, especially in the invertebrates, it is first of all necessary to undertake fundamental taxonomic work before any attempt at ecology is made. There are keys to the identification of some groups of animals in some parts of tropical Africa; some of these are published in inaccessible journals, and it is thus important that research libraries should be started and developed wherever possible. Reference collections of named animals may also be used in solving problems of identification of species. Until recently there was little attempt to build up scientific collections within tropical Africa; most specimens were sent to Europe and North America, but now several museums and universities have good named collections of the local fauna. Such collections are invaluable to the research worker in ecology.

It would seem then that, despite some disadvantages, there are enormous opportunities for ecological work in the African tropics, and it has been my intention in this book to draw attention to some of them.

Glossary

The terms below are defined in the way they are used in this book. Some terms can be used in a variety of ways depending upon the context; the definitions given below are those used by most animal ecologists.

aestivation: reduced activity of an animal associated with metabolic adjustments to hot or dry weather.

allele: an alternative form of a gene at a given locus on a chromosome.

anadromesis: up-river migration of fish.

apostatic selection: natural selection for genetic traits that stand out from or contrast with the normal.

assortative mating: selective mating of like genetic forms in a population.

Batesian mimicry: the resemblance of a palatable mimic to an unpalatable model.

biomass: the product of the number of individuals in a population and their mean weight.

competition: an interaction of individuals or species resulting from utilisation of essential resources that are in short supply.

convergent evolution: the evolution of similar organisms from unrelated ancestors.

cryptic colours and patterns: colours and patterns that tend to conceal an animal by matching it to the background against which it lives.

delayed implantation: a delay between fertilisation and the implantation of the embryo in the uterus of a mammal.

density-dependent events: ecological events whose effect varies with the density of the population.

density-independent events: ecological events whose effect does not vary with the density of the population.

dispersion: the quantitative distribution of organisms in an area.

dominant: a genetic factor showing in the phenotype when the genes controlling it are in either the heterozygous or the homozygous state.

endemic: of organisms: found only in a particular restricted area.

endoparasite: a parasite living inside the host animal.

endogenous rhythm: a physiological rhythm determined by the internal condition of the organism.

epiphragm : a thin, fragile, muco-calcareous secretion over the aperture of the shell of a land snail.

evolution : a cumulative inheritable change in a population.

exogenous rhythm : a physiological rhythm in an organism determined by external environmental factors.

fitness : a measure of the capacity of an individual or population to reproduce.

gene : an inheritable character that segregates in a Mendelian manner.

genotype : the genetic constitution of an organism.

heterozygote : an individual with different alleles at the homologous loci of a given pair of chromosomes.

homozygote : an individual with identical alleles at homologous loci of a given pair of chromosomes.

irruption : an irregular mass movement of a population.

linked genes : genes that tend to segregate together because they are on the same chromosome.

lunar periodicity : periodic fluctuations in biological events associated with a particular phase of the moon.

melanin : a dark pigment formed by the oxidation of the amino acid, tyrosine.

migration : a regular movement by individuals or populations to and from a breeding area.

mimicry : superficial resemblance of organisms of different species such that one or both benefits.

mode : a peak on a graph or histogram.

monotypic : of a taxonomic category: containing only one species.

Müllerian mimicry : the resemblance of several, often unrelated, unpalatable species.

mutation : a sudden and haphazard change in a gene.

natural selection : the non-random elimination of individuals (and therefore of genes) from a population; often abbreviated to *selection*.

niche : the sum of environmental factors into which an organism fits; the way in which an organism utilises its environment.

passerine : a perching or song bird.

phenotype : the appearance of an organism.

polygenic : of a character: determined by several or many genes.

polymodal variation : variation within a population with two or more modes in its distribution.

polymorphism : the occurrence together in the same population of two or more distinct genetic forms in such proportions that the rarest of them cannot be maintained by recurrent mutation alone.

polyoestrus : of female mammals: cyclical changes in behaviour that permit mating more than once a year.

population : a group of organisms of the same species living together.

proximate factors : environmental factors that stimulate periodic events in the lives of animals; biological triggers.

pterygote insect : a winged or secondarily wingless insect.

quadrat : a square used in sampling a population of relatively sedentary organisms.

recessive : a genetic factor which shows in the phenotype only when the genes controlling it are homozygous.

savanna : open grassy country with scattered trees and clumps of bushes.

sex-limited : of a gene that is present in both sexes but expresses itself in the phenotype of one sex only.

speciation : the evolutionary process by which new species are formed.

specific search image : a predator's 'pictorial' memory of the appearance of prey.

statistically significant : of a difference between two or more sets of figures that is not the result of chance alone.

subspecies : local, geographical variation in a species; the word *race* has the same meaning.

symbiosis : a biological association of two or more species resulting in mutual benefit.

sympatric : occurring in the same place.

taxonomy : the study of naming and classifying organisms.

territory : an area defended by an individual against other members of the same species.

ultimate factors : environmental factors that determine why an organism breeds, migrates, etc. at a particular time.

References

ADDERLEY, E. E. and BOWEN, E. G. 1962. Lunar component in precipitation data. *Science*, **137**: 749–50.

BEADLE, L. C. 1933. Scientific results of the Cambridge expedition to the East African lakes, 1930–1. 13. Adaptation to aerial respiration in *Alma emini* Mich., an oligochaet from East African swamps. *J. Linn. Soc.*, **38**: 347–50.

——— 1961. Adaptations of some aquatic animals to low oxygen levels and to anaerobic conditions. *Symp. Soc. exp. Biol.*, **15**: 120–31.

BERE, R. M. 1962. *The Wild Mammals of Uganda and Neighbouring Regions of East Africa*. Longmans, Green & Co., London.

BERRIE, A. D. and VISSER, S. A. 1963. Investigations of a growth-inhibiting substance affecting a natural population of freshwater snails. *Physiol. Zoöl.*, **36**: 167–73.

BOURLIÈRE, F. 1963. Observations on the ecology of some large African mammals. *African Ecology and Human Evolution*, **36**: 43–54.

BROOKS, J. L. 1950. Speciation in ancient lakes. *Quart. Rev. Biol.*, **25**: 131–76.

BROWN, L. H. 1955. Supplementary notes on the biology of the large birds of prey of Embu District, Kenya Colony. *Ibis*, **97**: 38–64.

BUECHNER, H. K. 1961. Territorial behavior in Uganda kob. *Science*, **133**: 698–9.

BUSS, I. O. 1961. Some observations on food habits and behavior of the African elephant. *J. Wildlife Mgmt.*, **25**: 131–48.

CARPENTER, G. D. H. 1949. *Pseudacraea eurytus* (L.) (Lep. Nymphalidae): A study of a polymorphic mimic in various degrees of speciation. *Trans. Roy. ent. Soc. London*, **100**: 71–133.

CARTER, C. O. 1962. *Human Heredity*. Penguin Books, Harmondsworth.

CHAPIN, J. P. 1932. The birds of the Belgian Congo, Part 1. *Bull. Amer. Mus. nat. Hist.*, **65**: 1–756.

CHAPMAN, B. M. and CHAPMAN, R. F. 1964. Observations on the biology of the lizard *Agama agama* in Ghana. *Proc. zool. Soc. London*, **143**: 121–32.

CLARKE, B. 1962. Balanced polymorphism and the diversity of sympatric species. *Publs. Syst. Ass.*, **4**: 47–70.

CORBET, P. S. 1958. Lunar periodicity of aquatic insects in Lake Victoria. *Nature, Lond.*, **182**: 330–1.

CORBET, P. S. and HADDOW, A. J. 1962. Diptera swarming high above the forest canopy in Uganda, with special reference to Tabanidae. *Trans. Roy. ent. Soc. London*, **114**: 267–84.

COTT, H. B. 1961. Scientific results of an inquiry into the ecology and economic status of the Nile crocodile (*Crocodilus niloticus*) in Uganda and Northern Rhodesia. *Trans. zool. Soc. London*, **29**: 211–356.

FORD, E. B. 1964. *Ecological Genetics*. Methuen, London.

FRYER, G. 1956. A report on the parasitic Copepoda and Branchiura of the fishes of Lake Nyasa. *Proc. zool. Soc. London*, **127**: 293–344.

— 1959. The trophic interrelationships and ecology of some littoral communities of Lake Nyasa with especial reference to the fishes, and a discussion of the evolution of a group of rock-frequenting Cichlidae. *Proc. zool. Soc. London*, **132**: 153–281.

— 1961. Observations on the biology of the cichlid fish *Tilapia variabilis* Boulenger in the northern waters of Lake Victoria (East Africa). *Revue zool. Bot. afr.*, **64**: 1–33.

GARRETT-JONES, C. 1951. The Congo floor maggot, *Auchmeromyia luteola* (F.), in a laboratory culture. *Bull. ent. Res.*, **41**: 679–708.

GLASGOW, J. P. 1963. *The Distribution and Abundance of Tsetse*. Pergamon Press, London.

GREEN, J. 1964. The numbers and distribution of the African fish eagle *Haliaëtus vocifer* on the eastern shores of Lake Albert. *Ibis*, **106**: 125–8.

GREENWOOD, P. H. 1958. Reproduction in the East African lung-fish *Protopterus aethiopicus* Heckel. *Proc. zool. Soc. London*, **130**: 547–67.

HADDOW, A. J. 1952. Field and laboratory studies on an African monkey, *Cercopithecus ascanius* Matschie. *Proc. zool. Soc. London*, **122**: 297–394.

— 1961. Entomological studies from a high tower in Mpanga Forest, Uganda. VII. The biting behaviour of mosquitoes and tabanids. *Trans. Roy. ent. Soc. London*, **113**: 315–35.

HADDOW, A. J., CORBET, P. S., GILLET, J. D., DIRMHIRN, I., JACKSON, T. H. E. and BROWN, K. W. 1961. Entomological studies from a high tower in Mpanga Forest, Uganda. *Trans. Roy. ent. Soc. London*, **113**: 249–368.

HADDOW, A. J., DAVIES, C. W. and WALKER, A. J. 1960. O'nyong-nyong fever: an epidemic virus disease in East Africa. *Trans. Roy. Soc. trop. Med. Hyg.*, **54**: 517–22.

HALL, B. P. and MOREAU, R. E. 1962. A study of the rare birds of Africa. *Bull. Brit. Mus. nat. Hist. Zool.*, **8**: 313–78.

HARRISON, G. A., WEINER, J. S., TANNER, J. M. and BARNICOT, N. A. 1964. *Human Biology. An Introduction to Human Evolution, Variation and Growth*. Oxford University Press, London.

HARTLAND-ROWE, R. 1955. Lunar rhythm in the emergence of an ephemeropteran. *Nature, Lond.*, **176**: 657.

HOLLINGSWORTH, M. J. 1960. The birth weights of African and European babies born in Ghana. *W. Afr. med. J.*, **9**: 256–9.

HOWES, N. H. and WELLS, G. P. 1934. The water relations of snails and slugs. *J. exp. Biol.*, **11**: 327–51.

JACKSON, T. H. E. 1961. Entomological studies from a high tower in Mpanga Forest, Uganda. IX. Observations on Lepidoptera (Rhopalocera). *Trans. Roy. ent. Soc. London*, **113**: 346–50.

JOHNELS, A. G. and SVENSSON, G. S. O. 1954. On the biology of *Protopterus annectens* (Owen). *Ark. Zool.*, **7**: 131–64.

JONES, T. S. and CAVE, A. J. E. 1960. Diet, longevity and dental disease in the Sierra Leone chimpanzee. *Proc. zool. Soc. London*, **135**: 147–55.

KEAY, R. W. J. 1959. *Vegetation Map of Africa*. Oxford University Press, London.

KELLAS, L. M. 1955. Observations on the reproductive activities, measurements, and growth rate of the dikdik (*Rhynchotragus kirkii thomasi* Neumann). *Proc. zool. Soc. London*, **124**: 751–84.

KLOPFER, P. H. and MACARTHUR, R. H. 1961. On the causes of tropical species diversity: niche overlap. *Amer. Nat.*, **95**: 223–6.

KOSSWIG, C. 1947. Selective mating as a factor for speciation in cichlid fish of East African lakes. *Nature, Lond.*, **159**: 604–5.

KÜHME, W. 1965. Communal food distribution and the division of labour in African hunting dogs. *Nature. Lond.*, **205**: 443–4.

LACK, D. 1954. *The Natural Regulation of Animal Numbers*. Oxford University Press, London.

LIVINGSTONE, F. B. 1962. Population genetics and population ecology. *Amer. Anthrop.*, **64**: 44–53.

LOWE, R. H. 1956. The breeding behaviour of *Tilapia* species (Pisces; Cichlidae) in natural waters: observations on *T. karomo* Poll and *T. variabilis* Boulenger. *Behaviour*, **9**: 140–63.

McCRAE, A. W. R. and VISSER, S. A. 1963. Recent 'Nairobi eye' beetle (*Paederus sabaeus* Er.) outbreaks in Uganda, and studies on the vesicating toxin. *Biochem. J.*, **89**: 79.

MACDONALD, W. W. 1956. Observations on the biology of chaorobids and chironomids in Lake Victoria and on the feeding habits of the 'elephant-snout fish' (*Mormyrus kannume* Forsk.). *J. Anim. Ecol.*, **25**: 36–53.

MACFADYEN, A. 1963. *Animal Ecology: Aims and Methods*. Pitman, London.

MACKWORTH-PRAED, C. W. and GRANT, C. H. B. 1952. *Birds of Eastern and North Eastern Africa*, vol. 1. Longmans, Green & Co., London.

MARLIER, G. 1955. Un trichoptère pélagique nouveau du lac Tanganika. *Revue zool. Bot. afr.*, **52**: 150–5.

MARSHALL, A. J. and WILLIAMS, M. C. 1959. The pre-nuptial migration of the yellow wagtail (*Motacilla flava*) from latitude 0° 04′ N. *Proc. zool. Soc. London*, **132**: 313–20.

MEAD, A. R. 1961. *The Giant African Snail: A Problem in Economic Malacology.* University of Chicago Press, Chicago.

MOREAU, R. E. 1948. Ecological isolation in a rich tropical avifauna. *J. Anim. Ecol.*, **17**: 113–26.

1952. Africa since the mesozoic: with particular reference to certain biological problems. *Proc. zool Soc. London*, **121**: 869–913.

1954. The distribution of African evergreen-forest birds. *Proc. Linn. Soc. London*, **165**: 35–46.

1963. The distribution of tropical African birds as an indicator of past climatic changes. *African Ecology and Human Evolution*, **36**: 28–42.

MUTERE, F. A. 1965. Delayed implantation in an equatorial fruit bat. *Nature, Lond.*, **207**: 780.

NORRIS, M. J. 1962. Diapause induced by photoperiod in a tropical locust, *Nomadacris septemfasciata* (Serv.). *Proc. Ass. appl. Biol.*, **50**: 600–603.

NORTH, M. E. W. 1963. Breeding of the black-headed herons at Nairobi, Kenya, 1958–62. *J. East Afr. nat. Hist. Soc.*, **24**: 33–63.

ODHIAMBO, T. R. 1958. Drosophilidae (Dipt.) breeding in cercopid (Hem.) spittle masses. *Entomologist's mon. Mag.*, **94**: 17.

OGILVIE, P. W. and OWEN, D. F. 1964. Colour change and polymorphism in *Chameleo bitaeniatus*. *Nature, Lond.*, **202**: 209–10.

OWEN, D. F. 1963. Polymorphism and population density in the African land snail, *Limicolaria martensiana*. *Science*, **140**: 666–7.

1964. Bimodal occurrence of breeding in an equatorial land snail. *Ecology*, **45**: 862.

PERRY, J. S. 1953. The reproduction of the African elephant, *Loxodonta africana*. *Phil. Trans. Roy. Soc. London*, **237**: 93–149.

PHILLIPS, J. 1959. *Agriculture and Ecology in Africa.* Faber and Faber, London.

RUTISHAUSER, I. H. E. 1962. The food of the Baganda. *Uganda Mus. Occas. Pap.*, **6**: 1–19.

SALT, G. 1952. The arthropod population of the soil in some East African pastures. *Bull. ent. Res.*, **43**: 203–220.

1954. A contribution to the ecology of Upper Kilimanjaro. *J. Ecol.*, **42**: 375–423.

SCHALLER, G. B. 1963. *The Mountain Gorilla.* University of Chicago Press, Chicago.

STEWART, D. R. M. and STEWART, J. 1963. The distribution of some large mammals in Kenya. *J. East Afr. nat. Hist. Soc.*, **24**: 1–52.

SWYNNERTON, G. H. and HAYMAN, R. W. 1950–51. A check list of the land mammals of the Tanganyika Territory and the Zanzibar Protectorate. *J. East Afr. nat. Hist. Soc.*, **20**: 274–392.

THOMAS, I. F. 1961. The Cladocera of the swamps of Uganda. *Crustaceana*, **2**: 108–125.

WALLACE, A. R. 1878. *Tropical Nature and other Essays*. MacMillan, London.

WARD, P. 1965. Feeding ecology of the black-faced dioch *Quelea quelea* in Nigeria. *Ibis*, **107**: 173–214.

WASAWO, D. P. S. 1959. A dry season burrow of *Protopterus aethiopicus* Heckel. *Revue zool. Bot. afr.*, **60**: 65–71.

WILLIAMS, C. B. 1951. The migrations of libytheine butterflies in Africa. *Nig. Field*, **16**: 152–9.

1964. *Patterns in the Balance of Nature and Related Problems in Quantitative Ecology*. Academic Press, London.

Index

Roman numbers refer to Plates